Name:

ABOUT THE BAKER'S FUN-SCHOOLING JOURNAL

The Baker's Fun-Schooling Journal is a curriculum handbook that covers a number of school subjects, while focusing on baking. Students will work through Baking Challenges, try new recipes, and get to be creative.

To complete this guided learning journal, students need books, baking supplies, and films/documentaries. This journal can be used daily for an intensive baking unit lasting about a month or once a week to last all school year.

This book includes lots of "unhealthy" sweets made with common ingredients.
One of the first activities will prompt the student to choose substitutes for those ingredients.
As the student tries new recipes, please encourage them to modify them to suit your family's healthy eating plan. Students learn valuable skills through substitutions and alternatives.

Thinking Tree Learning Levels: B2, C1, C2. Ages 10+, younger with assistance.
Companion books: Yum-Schooling and Smoothie Time.

CHILDREN SHOULD BE SUPERVISED WHEN COOKING AND SHOULD USE SAFETY EQUIPMENT.

TOPICS COVERED INCLUDE:

Planning & setting priorities

Baking challenges

Creative thinking

Drawing

Reading

Film study

Math practice

And more!

The Thinking Tree

The Baker's FUN-SCHOOLING JOURNAL

HOMESCHOOLING CURRICULUM HANDBOOK

FOR Students Majoring in Baking

Anna Miriam Brown

Sarah Janisse Brown

FunSchooling.com

Instructions

Draw or list six things you want to learn about or baking skills you want to master:

1.

2.

3.

4.

5.

6.

Action Steps:

1. Go to the library, your bookshelf, or a bookstore.

2. Choose a total of nine books about these topics or skills.

3. Gather your supplies and get creative!

4. Use 5 pages each day to develop your skills as a baker.

Supplies Needed:

You will need pencils, colored pencils and/or gel pens, baking supplies, a kitchen, the ingredients, and films/documentaries.

CHOOSE YOUR BOOKS

Pick out 9 different books that will help you study baking.

DRAW tHE COVERS anD tItLES HERE:

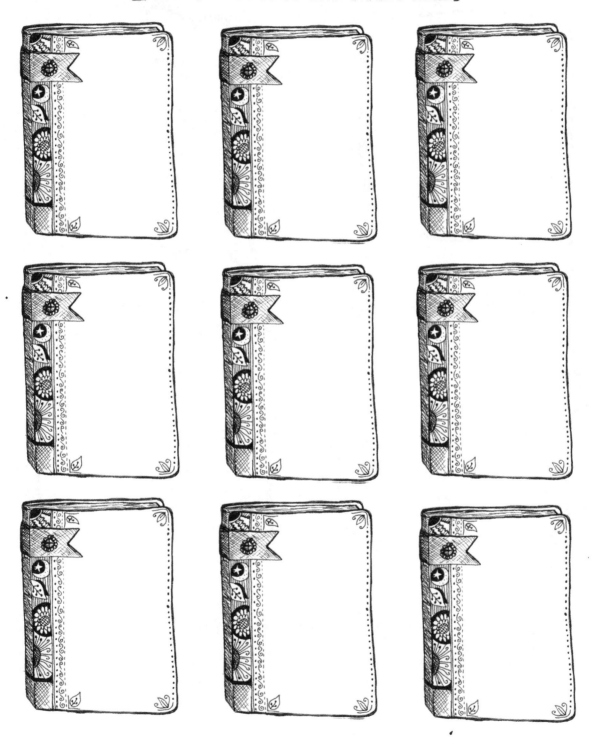

Plans & Priorities

Date:_____

To-do List:
_____
_____
_____
_____
_____

A Quote:
_____
_____
_____
_____

Shopping List:
_____
_____
_____
_____

My Plans:
_____
_____
_____
_____

I am Thankful for:
_____
_____
_____
_____

Relax & Be Creative

Baking Challenge

Research substitutes to common ingredients.
Change one of your favorite recipes using some of these alternatives:

Instead of this:	Try this:
one egg	
one cup white flour	
one cup sugar	
one cup vegetable oil	
one cup whipped topping	
one cup milk	
one cup butter	

How did it come out?

How many stars do you give your work?

Notes:_____

Reading Time!

Choose a few books from your stack to focus on today. Write down or draw anything that inspires you.

Screen Time

Watch a cooking show, high-quality film, video, documentary, or baking tutorial.

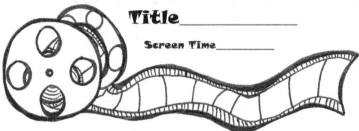

Title_____

Screen Time_____

Notes

Take notes on what you are learning.

_____

_____

_____

_____

_____

_____

_____

Rating:

Worst

Bad

Awful

Ok

Nice

Great

Best

Math Practice

Use this page for math practice, graphic design, and creative measurements. If you have a book on mathematics use this page for notes.

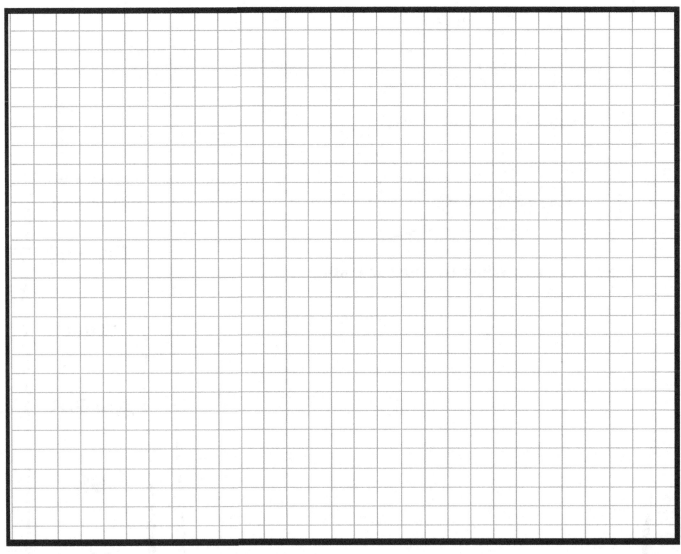

Notes:_____

_____

_____

_____

_____

_____

_____

Baking Dreams

Design something beautiful you want to bake!

Look at photos in your cookbooks or online for ideas.

Notes:_____

_____

_____

_____

_____

_____

SINCE 1991

BAKERY

• PREMIUM GOODS •

No-bake Raspberry Cheesecakes

Ingredients:

- 1 cup raspberry puree, strained

- 12 oz. cream cheese

- 1 1/2 cups whipped topping

- 1/2 cup powdered sugar, sifted

- 1 cup crushed graham cracker crumbs

- ¾ cup raspberries

- 1 tsp vanilla extract

- whipped cream, optional garnish

Instructions:

Fill the bottom of six small cups
with the crushed graham crackers.
Crush or blend the raspberries
to make the puree and set aside.
Whip the cream cheese until smooth with an electric mixer,
then mix in the raspberry puree,
vanilla extract, and powdered sugar.
Lastly, fold in the whipped topping
and spoon into the prepared cups.
Top with a sprinkle of crushed graham crackers,
raspberries, and whipped cream. ENJOY!

How many stars do you give this recipe?

Baking Time!

Notes:_____

_____

_____

_____

_____

_____

Plans & Priorities

Date:_____

To-do List:
_____
_____
_____
_____

A Quote:
_____
_____
_____
_____

Shopping List:
_____
_____
_____
_____

My Plans:
_____
_____
_____
_____

I am Thankful for:
_____
_____
_____
_____

Relax & Be Creative

Baking Challenge

Ask your parents or relatives for a special
family recipe to try.

Draw what you've made!

How many stars do you give your work?

Notes:_____

Reading Time!

Choose a few books from your stack to focus on today. Write down or draw anything that inspires you.

Screen Time

Watch a cooking show, high-quality film, video, documentary, or baking tutorial.

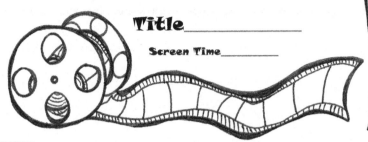

Title_____

Screen Time_____

Notes

Take notes on what you are learning.

_____
_____
_____
_____
_____
_____
_____

Rating:

Worst

Bad

Awful

Ok

Nice

Great

Best

Math Practice

Use this page for math practice, graphic design, and creative measurements. If you have a book on mathematics use this page for notes.

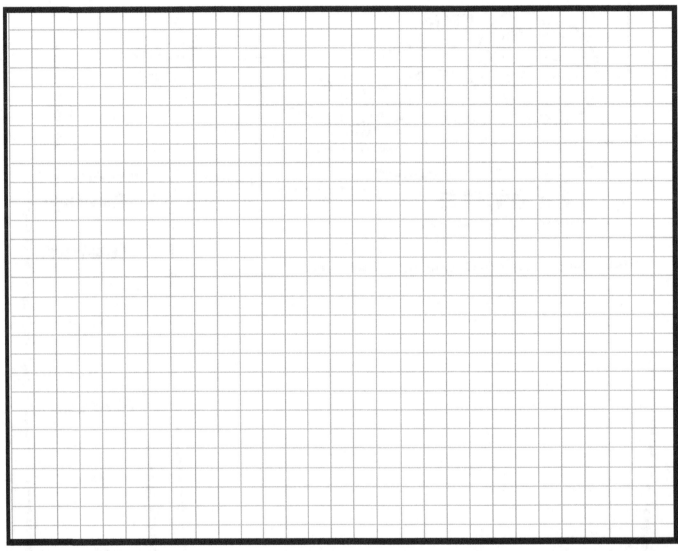

Notes:_____

_____

_____

_____

_____

_____

_____

_____

Baking Dreams

Design something beautiful you want to bake!

Look at photos in your cookbooks or online for ideas.

Notes:_____

_____

_____

_____

_____

_____

SINCE   1991

BAKERY

• PREMIUM GOODS •

M&M Blondies

Ingredients:

- 1/2 cup butter, softened

- 2 cups brown sugar

- 2 eggs

- 1 1/2 tsp vanilla

- 1 tsp salt

- 2 tsp baking powder

- 2 cups flour

- 1 1/2 cups M&M candies

Instructions:

Preheat the oven to 350°F
Spray a 9x13 baking dish with nonstick spray.
Beat the butter and brown sugar until creamy.
Add the eggs and vanilla and beat again.
Sift together the salt, baking powder, and flour.
Slowly beat into the butter mixture.
Stir in 1 cup of the M&M candies by hand.
Spread the batter in buttered dish.
Sprinkle the top with the extra 1/2 cup M&Ms.
Bake for 22-25 minutes.
Let the cookie bars cool and then cut into squares.

Serve and make everyone happy!

How many stars do you give this recipe?

Baking Time!

Notes: _____

_____

_____

_____

_____

_____

**Draw a picture of
your baking creation!**

Plans & Priorities

Date:_____

To-do List:
_____
_____
_____
_____

A Quote:
_____
_____
_____
_____

Shopping List:
_____
_____
_____
_____

My Plans:
_____
_____
_____
_____

I am Thankful for:

_____
_____
_____
_____

Baking Challenge

Watch a baking show and attempt the recipe at home!

Draw what you've made!

How many stars do you give your work?

Notes:_____

Reading Time!

Choose a few books from your stack to focus on today. Write down or draw anything that inspires you.

Screen Time

Watch a cooking show, high-quality film, video, documentary, or baking tutorial.

Title_____

Screen Time_____

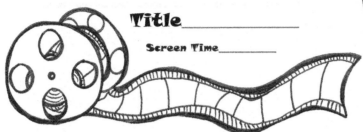

Notes

Take notes on what you are learning.

_____
_____
_____
_____
_____
_____
_____

Rating:

Worst

Bad

Awful

Ok

Nice

Great

Best

Math Practice

Use this page for math practice, graphic design, and creative measurements. If you have a book on mathematics use this page for notes.

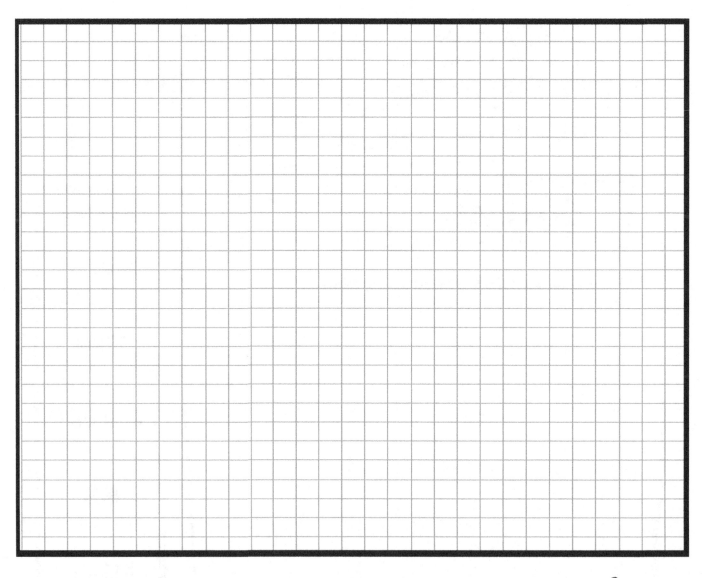

Notes:_____

_____

_____

_____

_____

_____

_____

_____

Baking Dreams

Design something beautiful you want to bake!

Look at photos in your cookbooks or online for ideas.

Notes:_____
_____
_____
_____
_____
_____

SINCE · 1991
BAKERY
· PREMIUM GOODS ·

Healthy Chocolate Cookies

Ingredients

- 2-3 medium bananas

- 1 1/2 cups quick oats

- 1/2 cup chocolate protein powder

- 2 tbsp unsweetened dark cocoa powder

- 1 tbsp chia seeds, optional

- 1 tsp vanilla

- 2 tbsp ground flaxseed, optional

- 2 tbsp mini chocolate chips

SINCE 1991

BAKERY

• PREMIUM GOODS •

Directions

Preheat the oven to 350°F.

Mash the bananas. Stir the oats, protein powder, cocoa powder, chia seeds, vanilla, and flaxseed into the bananas.

Drop the mixture into 15 even spoonfuls on a nonstick baking sheet or a pan lined with a parchment paper. Press each cookie flat. You can use your fingers to keep each cookie in a nice, round shape. Sprinkle the top of the cookies with the mini chocolate chips. Bake for 15 minutes.

Gently remove the cookies to parchment paper or a wire rack to cool completely before devouring.

How many stars do you give this recipe?

Baking Time!

Notes: _____

_____

_____

_____

_____

Draw a picture of your baking creation!

Plans & Priorities

Date:_____

To-do List:
_____
_____
_____
_____
_____

A Quote:
_____
_____
_____
_____

Shopping List:
_____
_____
_____
_____
_____

My Plans:
_____
_____
_____
_____

I am Thankful for:

_____
_____
_____
_____

Relax & Be Creative

Baking Challenge

Make a dessert pizza! Use cookie dough for the pizza dough and be creative with sweet toppings!

Draw what you've made!

How many stars do you give your work?

Notes:_____

Reading Time!

Choose a few books from your stack to focus on today. Write down or draw anything that inspires you.

Screen Time

Watch a cooking show, high-quality film, video, documentary, or baking tutorial.

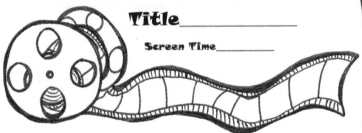

Title_____

Screen Time_____

Notes

Take notes on what you are learning.

_____
_____
_____
_____
_____
_____

Rating:

Worst

Bad

Awful

Ok

Nice

Great

Best

Math Practice

Use this page for math practice, graphic design, and creative measurements. If you have a book on mathematics use this page for notes.

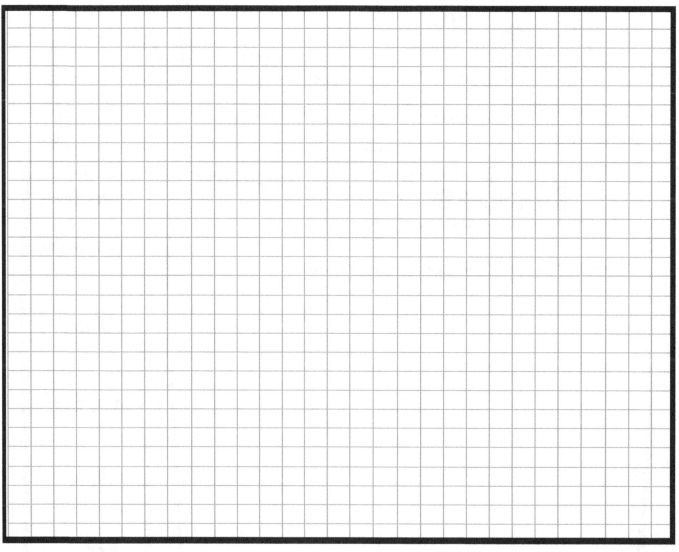

Notes:_____

_____

_____

_____

_____

_____

_____

_____

Baking Dreams

Design something beautiful you want to bake!

Look at photos in your cookbooks or online for ideas.

Notes:_____

_____

_____

_____

_____

_____

SINCE 1991

BAKERY

• PREMIUM GOODS •

Mini Key Lime Pies

Ingredients

- 2 large eggs

- 2/3 cup granulated sugar

- 1/2 cup key lime juice

- 1/4 cup un-salted butter

- 1 package Keebler Ready Crust mini Graham Cracker crusts

- 1 cup whipped topping

- 1 fresh key lime, cut into slices

- 6 raspberries

- 1 tsp vanilla

Instructions

Place a small saucepan with water on the stove and heat to a low boil.
Whisk together the eggs, sugar, vanilla, and key lime juice in a glass bowl.
Place the bowl over the top of the simmering water.
Make sure the bowl fits tightly, so the steam doesn't come out.
Stir the mixture constantly until it reaches 180 degrees
and thickens.
Remove from the heat and stir in the butter until smooth.
Spoon the key lime curd evenly into the mini Graham Cracker Crusts.
Press a small piece of plastic wrap on top of each pie,
directly on the surface. Refrigerate until chilled.
Remove the plastic wrap. Scoop whipped topping on top of each pie.
Top with a key lime slice and raspberry right before serving.

How many stars do you give this recipe?

Baking Time!

Notes:_____

_____

_____

_____

_____

_____

Draw a picture of
your baking creation!

Plans & Priorities

Date:_____

To-do List:

A Quote:

Shopping List:

My Plans:

I am Thankful for:

Baking Challenge

Make a healthy dessert for someone who is on a special diet.
Be sure to research what kind of diet they are on so you make
something they can actually eat!

Draw what you've made!

How many stars do you give your work?

Notes:_____

Reading Time!

Choose a few books from your stack to focus on today. Write down or draw anything that inspires you.

Screen Time

Watch a cooking show, high-quality film, video, documentary, or baking tutorial.

Title_____

Screen Time_____

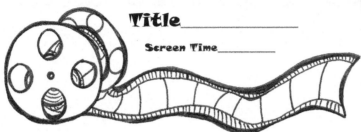

Notes

Take notes on what you are learning.

_____
_____
_____
_____
_____
_____
_____

Rating:

Worst

Bad

Awful

Ok

Nice

Great

Best

Math Practice

Use this page for math practice, graphic design,
and creative measurements. If you have a book on
mathematics use this page for notes.

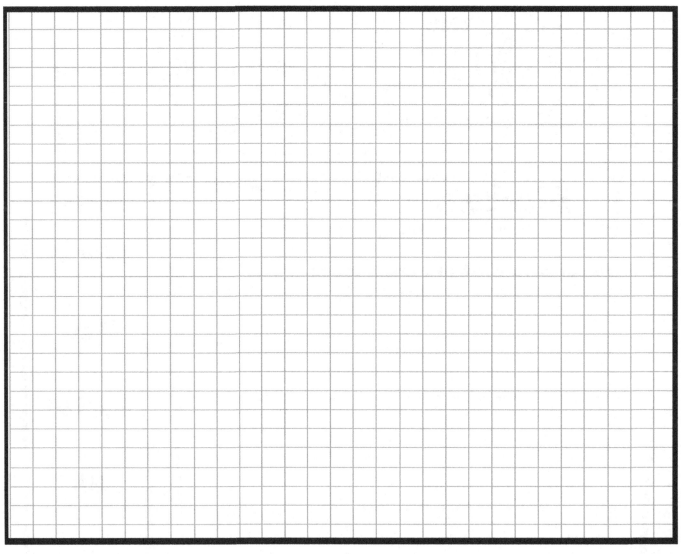

Notes:_____
_____
_____
_____
_____
_____
_____
_____

Baking Dreams

Design something beautiful you want to bake!

Look at photos in your cookbooks or online for ideas.

Notes:_____

_____

_____

_____

_____

_____

SINCE 1991

BAKERY

• PREMIUM GOODS •

Lazy Chocolate Chip Cookies

Ingredients

- 1 box yellow or white cake mix
- 2 eggs, beaten
- 1 tsp vanilla extract
- 1 stick butter melted
- 2 cups chocolate chips

SINCE 1991
BAKERY
• PREMIUM GOODS •

Instructions

Preheat oven to 350°F.
Spray a 9x13 inch pan with cooking spray.
for easy cutting and clean up.
Mix everything together.
Pour into the pan and bake for 20 min.

Yummy...

How many stars do you give this recipe?

Baking Time!

Notes: _____
_____
_____
_____
_____
_____

Draw a picture of
your baking creation!

Plans & Priorities

Date:_____

To-do List:
_____
_____
_____
_____
_____

A Quote:
_____
_____
_____
_____
_____

Shopping List:
_____
_____
_____
_____
_____

My Plans:
_____
_____
_____
_____

I am Thankful for:
_____
_____
_____
_____

Baking Challenge

Make a dessert that does not include sugar.
What will you use instead?
Maybe maple syrup, monk fruit, or stevia?

Draw what you've made!

How many stars do you give your work?

Notes:_____

Reading Time!

Choose a few books from your stack to focus on today. Write down or draw anything that inspires you.

Screen Time

Watch a cooking show, high-quality film, video, documentary, or baking tutorial.

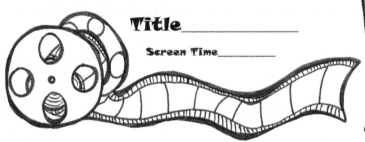

Title_____

Screen Time_____

Notes

Take notes on what you are learning.

_____

_____

_____

_____

_____

_____

_____

Rating:

Worst

Bad

Awful

Ok

Nice

Great

Best

Math Practice

Use this page for math practice, graphic design, and creative measurements. If you have a book on mathematics use this page for notes.

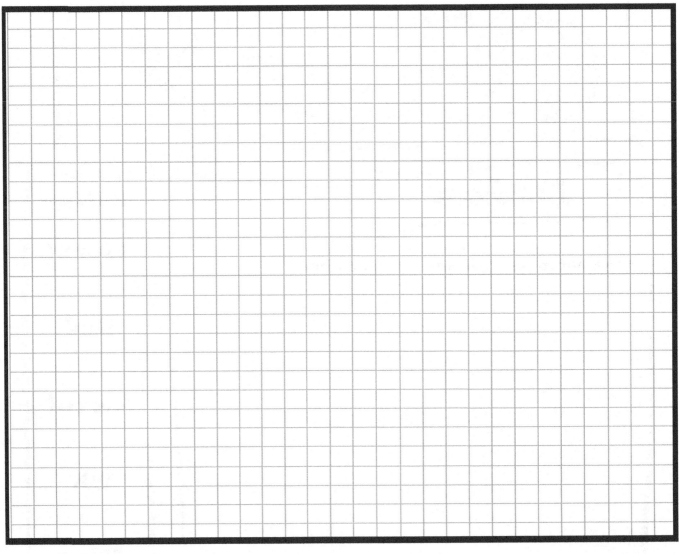

Notes:_____

_____

_____

_____

_____

_____

_____

Baking Dreams

Design something beautiful you want to bake!

Look at photos in your cookbooks or online for ideas.

Notes:_____

_____

_____

_____

_____

_____

SINCE 1991

BAKERY

• PREMIUM GOODS •

Ukrainian Crepes

Ingredients

- 1 cup all-purpose flour, sifted

- 1/4 tsp salt

- 2 eggs

- 1/2 cup milk

- 1/2 cup water

- 1 tsp vanilla (optional - add when making a sweet crepe)

- 2 1/2 tbsp butter, melted and cooled
- Oil or butter for frying

Instructions

In a large bowl whisk together eggs, milk,
water, vanilla, and butter. Sift in flour and salt
and whisk all ingredients together until batter is smooth.
Heat a 6-inch or larger skillet with oil or butter, just
enough to coat the pan, on a medium-high heat.
Pour 1/4 cup of butter and swirl batter in pan forming a
thin circular pancake.
Cook for about 2 minutes and flip to cook the other side.
Fill with ingredients of your choice.
(I love adding whipped cream and Nutella.)

How many stars do you give this recipe?

Baking Time!

Notes: _____
_____
_____
_____
_____

**Draw a picture of
your baking creation!**

Plans & Priorities

Date:_____

To-do List:
_____
_____
_____
_____

A Quote:
_____
_____
_____
_____

Shopping List:
_____
_____
_____
_____

My Plans:
_____
_____
_____
_____

I am Thankful for:
_____
_____
_____
_____

Baking Challenge

Make a dessert that includes three different candy bars. Be creative!
What will you make? Cheesecake? Cookies? Mousse?

Draw what you've made!

How many stars do you give your work?

Notes:_____

Reading Time!

Choose a few books from your stack to focus on today. Write down or draw anything that inspires you.

Screen Time

Watch a cooking show, high-quality film, video, documentary, or baking tutorial.

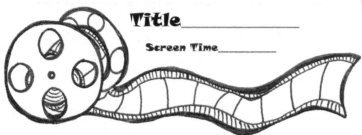

Title_____

Screen Time_____

Notes

Take notes on what you are learning.

_____
_____
_____
_____
_____
_____
_____

Rating:

Worst

Bad

Awful

Ok

Nice

Great

Best

Math Practice

Use this page for math practice, graphic design, and creative measurements. If you have a book on mathematics use this page for notes.

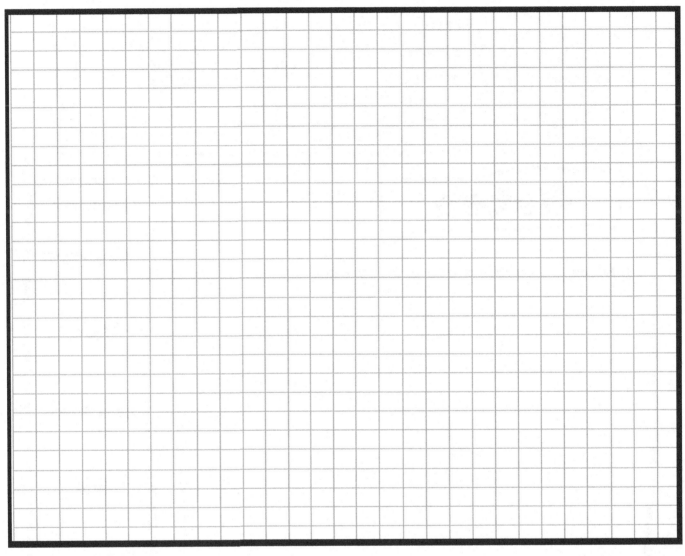

Notes:_____

_____

_____

_____

_____

_____

_____

_____

Baking Dreams

Design something beautiful you want to bake!

Look at photos in your cookbooks or online for ideas.

Notes:_____

_____

_____

_____

_____

_____

SINCE 1991

BAKERY
• PREMIUM GOODS •

Fresh Bread

Ingredients

- 2 tsp yeast
- 1/2 cup warm water
- 2 cups hot water
- 3 tbsp sugar
- 2 1/2 tsp salt
- 1/3 cup oil
- 6 1/2 cups bread flour
- 1 egg white for brushing on bread
- 1 tbsp brown sugar

Instructions

Preheat oven to 375°F.

In a small bowl, dissolve your yeast in ½ cup warm water.

Make sure that your water is warm (not too cold, not too hot).

Let sit for 10 minutes.

In a separate mixing bowl, combine hot water, sugar, salt, oil, and 3 cups of the flour and mix together. Add the yeast mixture to the bowl.

Add the remaining 3 1/2 cups of flour, one cup at a time, mixing after each addition. Watch for the dough to start pulling away from the bowl to know it's ready. Once all of the flour is added, let sit for 10 minutes.

Separate your dough into 3 pieces. On a floured surface, roll each piece into a 9x12 rectangle, like a jelly roll.

Next shape the dough into a French bread loaf and smooth out edges.

Place the dough on a greased baking pan.

Using a knife, make 3-4 diagonal cuts about 1/4 inch thick in the bread.

Brush with the beaten egg whites and brown sugar.

Let loaf rise uncovered for 30-40 minutes in a warm place.

Bake for 18-22 minutes or until golden brown. Butter and enjoy!

How many stars do you give this recipe?

Baking Time!

Notes: _____

_____

_____

_____

_____

Draw a picture of
your baking creation!

Plans & Priorities

Date:_____

To-do List:
_____
_____
_____
_____
_____

A Quote:
_____
_____
_____
_____
_____

Shopping List:
_____
_____
_____
_____
_____

My Plans:
_____
_____
_____
_____

I am Thankful for:
_____
_____
_____
_____

Relax & Be Creative

Baking Challenge

Make funnel cake!
It's much easier than you think.
Heat up a pan with about a half inch of coconut oil.
Pour pancake batter into a bag with a small hole at the bottom, squirt the batter into the pan in swirls, then flip once when one side is golden brown. After the 2nd side is browned, carefully move your beautiful funnel cake to a plate with a paper towel. After it cools a bit, sprinkle with powdered sugar and enjoy! Add cinnamon to the sugar for a cinnamon roll taste.

Draw what you've made!

How many stars do you give your work?

Notes:_____

Reading Time!

Choose a few books from your stack
to focus on today. Write down or draw
anything that inspires you.

Screen Time

Watch a cooking show, high-quality film, video, documentary, or baking tutorial.

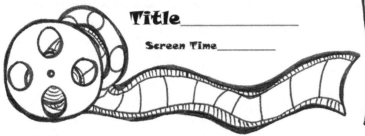

Title_____

Screen Time_____

Notes

Take notes on what you are learning.

_____
_____
_____
_____
_____
_____
_____

Rating:

Worst

Bad

Awful

Ok

Nice

Great

Best

Math Practice

Use this page for math practice, graphic design, and creative measurements. If you have a book on mathematics use this page for notes.

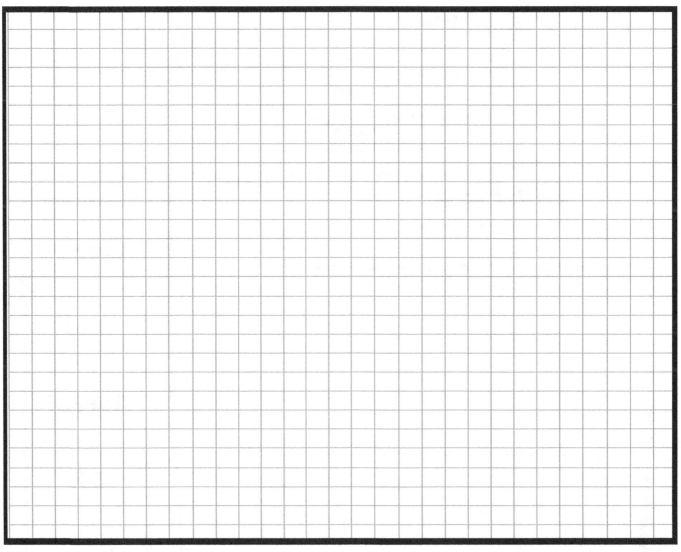

Notes:_____

_____

_____

_____

_____

_____

_____

_____

Baking Dreams

Design something beautiful you want to bake!

Look at photos in your cookbooks or online for ideas.

Notes:_____

_____

_____

_____

_____

_____

SINCE 1991

BAKERY

• PREMIUM GOODS •

Soft and Chewy Snickerdoodles

Ingredients

- 1 cup unsalted butter, softened
- 1¼ cups granulated sugar
- ¼ cup brown sugar
- 2 eggs
- ½ tsp vanilla extract
- 2¾ cups all-purpose flour
- 2 tsp baking powder
- ½ tsp salt
- 1 tsp cinnamon

Cinnamon Sugar Coating

- 5 tbsp granulated sugar
- 2 tsp cinnamon

Instructions

Preheat oven to 350°F.

Using a mixer, cream together the butter, sugar, and brown sugar. Add in the eggs one at a time and mix after each egg is added. Then add the vanilla extract and mix until combined.

In a different medium bowl, mix together the flour, baking powder, salt, and 1 tsp cinnamon.

Gradually add the dry ingredients to the wet mixture and mix until combined.

Optional step: To make it easier to roll the dough into balls, cover the bowl with plastic wrap and place in the refrigerator for 15 minutes.

Make the cinnamon sugar topping by combining the 5 tablespoons sugar and 2 teaspoons cinnamon in a small bowl.

Roll the dough into 1-inch balls. Then roll the balls in the cinnamon sugar mixture and place them on a cookie sheet that has been prepared with parchment paper. Bake cookies for 8-10 minutes.

How many stars do you give this recipe?

Baking Time!

Notes: _____

_____

_____

_____

_____

_____

Plans & Priorities

Date:_____

To-do List:
_____
_____
_____
_____
_____

A Quote:
_____
_____
_____
_____

Shopping List:
_____
_____
_____
_____
_____

My Plans:
_____
_____
_____
_____

I am Thankful for:
_____
_____
_____
_____

Baking Challenge

Try to make something delicious out of four ingredients.
What ingredients will you use?

Draw what you've made!

How many stars do you give your work?

Notes:

Reading Time!

Choose a few books from your stack to focus on today. Write down or draw anything that inspires you.

Screen Time

Watch a cooking show, high-quality film, video, documentary, or baking tutorial.

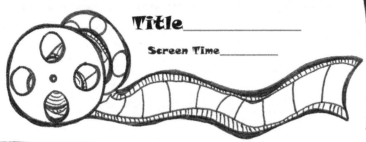

Title_____

Screen Time_____

Notes

Take notes on what you are learning.

_____

_____

_____

_____

_____

_____

_____

Rating:

Worst

Bad

Awful

Ok

Nice

Great

Best

Math Practice

Use this page for math practice, graphic design, and creative measurements. If you have a book on mathematics use this page for notes.

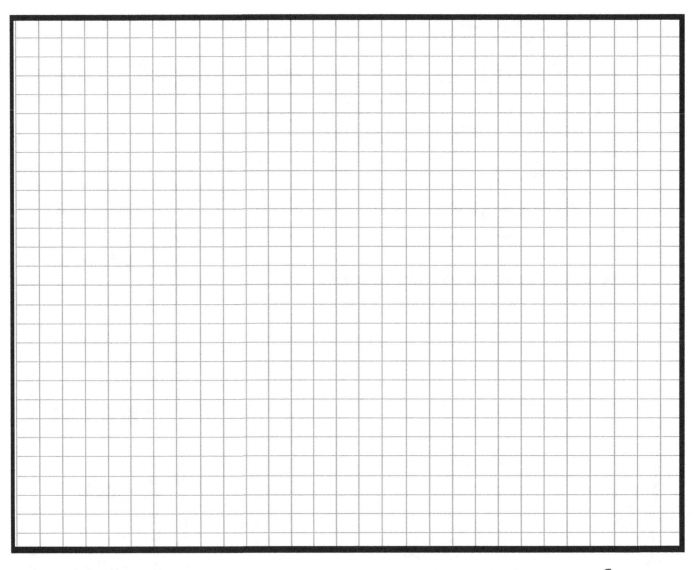

Notes:_____

_____

_____

_____

_____

_____

_____

Baking Dreams

Design something beautiful you want to bake!

Look at photos in your cookbooks or online for ideas.

Notes:_____

_____

_____

_____

_____

_____

SINCE 1991

BAKERY

• PREMIUM GOODS •

Strawberry Cheesecake Muffins

Ingredients
- 2 cups all-purpose flour

- 1/2 tsp salt

- 3 tsp baking powder

- 1/2 cup cold un-salted butter

- 1/2 cup granulated sugar, plus a little extra for sprinkling on top

- 1 cup milk

- 1 cup cream cheese

- 2 1/2 cups chopped strawberries, washed and chopped into 1/8 inch chunks

Instructions
Preheat oven to 400°F.

In a large mixing bowl, sift flour, salt, and baking powder.

Cut butter into small pieces and mix into flour with a pastry cutter (or two knives, or your hands) until the mixture is crumbly.

Stir in sugar. Add milk and stir until just combined.

Gently fold in chopped strawberries.

Scoop into well greased or parchment-lined muffin tins, spoon about a teaspoon of cream cheese into each muffin, sprinkle tops with a pinch of sugar each, and bake at 400 for 20 minutes.

The tops will be slightly golden and a toothpick or fork inserted should come out clean.

Baking Time!

Notes: _____

_____

_____

_____

_____

_____

**Draw a picture of
your baking creation!**

Plans & Priorities

Date:_____

To-do List:
_____
_____
_____
_____
_____

A Quote:
_____
_____
_____
_____

Shopping List:
_____
_____
_____
_____

My Plans:
_____
_____
_____
_____

I am Thankful for:
_____
_____
_____
_____

Relax & Be Creative

Baking Challenge

Do the "take-out Challenge", and no, I'm not talking about fast food. First, find a Chocolate chip Cookie recipe. Make four or more batches, but with each batch, remove a key ingredient, like baking powder, brown sugar, eggs, or butter, and then bake all the Cookies. This will literally take you to the next level of understanding the science behind each ingredient and will help you be a better off-recipe baker. You can try to do this with other desserts too, like Cake.

Draw what you've made!

How many stars do you give your work?

Notes:_____

Reading Time!

Choose a few books from your stack to focus on today. Write down or draw anything that inspires you.

Screen Time

Watch a cooking show, high-quality film, video, documentary, or baking tutorial.

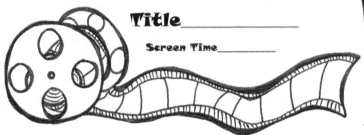

Title_____

Screen Time_____

Notes

Take notes on what you are learning.

_____
_____
_____
_____
_____
_____
_____

Rating:

Worst

Bad

Awful

Ok

Nice

Great

Best

Math Practice

Use this page for math practice, graphic design,
and creative measurements. If you have a book on
mathematics use this page for notes.

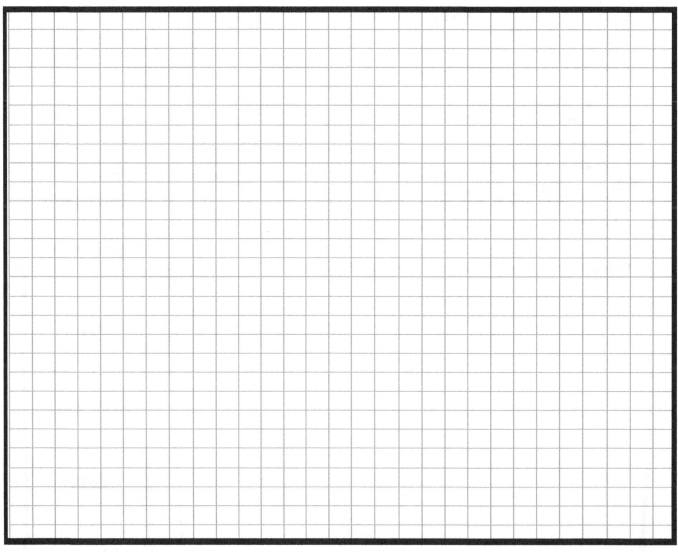

Notes:_____
_____
_____
_____
_____
_____
_____
_____

Baking Dreams

Design something beautiful you want to bake!

Look at photos in your cookbooks or online for ideas.

Notes:_____

_____

_____

_____

_____

_____

SINCE 1991

BAKERY

• PREMIUM GOODS •

Cookies and Cream Cupcakes

Ingredients

Cupcakes
- 1 chocolate box cake mix
- 1 small instant chocolate pudding
- 1 cup sour cream
- 1 cup vegetable oil
- 4 eggs
- 1/2 cup milk
- 1 tbsp vanilla
- 1 cup mini chocolate chips

Frosting and Filling
- 2 - 8oz Cream cheese, softened
- 1 - 2lb bag powdered sugar
- 1 tbsp vanilla
- 1 - 8oz tub whipped topping
- 15 finely crushed Oreos, plus 6 Oreos separated into halves

Instructions

Cupcakes
Preheat oven to 350°F.
Beat all ingredients, except the chocolate chips, for 2 minutes.
Fold in chocolate chips.
Fill cupcake liners half full. Bake for about 16 minutes or until toothpick inserted in center comes out clean. Let cool completely before eating.

Filling and Frosting
Beat cream cheese and vanilla until smooth. Beat in powdered sugar. Fold in whipped topping and crushed Oreos. Refrigerate for an hour before decorating cupcakes. Plop a mound of leftover filling on top. Decorate with an extra half Oreo.

How many stars do you give this recipe?

Baking Time!

Notes: _____

_____

_____

_____

_____

_____

**Draw a picture of
your baking creation!**

Plans & Priorities

Date:_____

To-do List:
_____
_____
_____
_____

A Quote:
_____
_____
_____
_____

Shopping List:
_____
_____
_____
_____

My Plans:
_____
_____
_____
_____

I am Thankful for:
_____
_____
_____
_____

Baking Challenge

Make a popular Mexican dessert.

Draw what you've made!

How many stars do you give your work?

Notes:_____

Reading Time!

Choose a few books from your stack to focus on today. Write down or draw anything that inspires you.

Screen Time

Watch a cooking show, high-quality film, video, documentary, or baking tutorial.

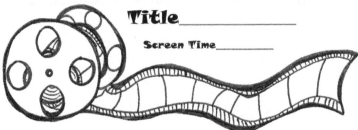

Title_____

Screen Time_____

Notes

Take notes on what you are learning.

_____
_____
_____
_____
_____
_____
_____

Rating:

Worst

Bad

Awful

Ok

Nice

Great

Best

Math Practice

Use this page for math practice, graphic design, and creative measurements. If you have a book on mathematics use this page for notes.

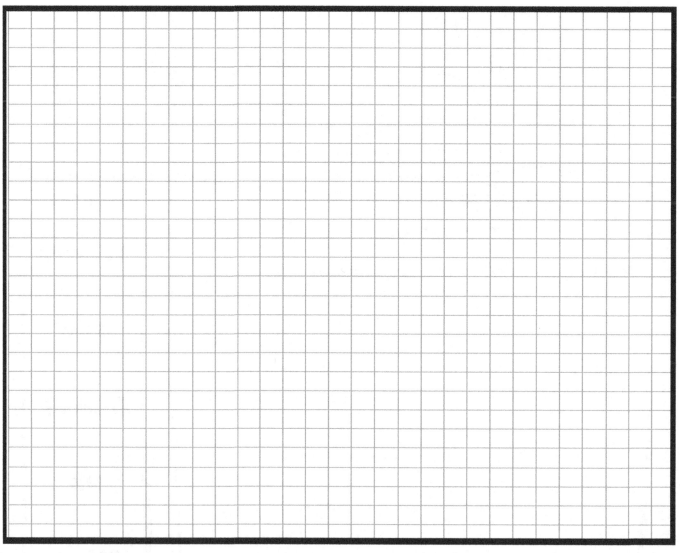

Notes:_____

_____

_____

_____

_____

_____

_____

Baking Dreams

Design something beautiful you want to bake!

Look at photos in your cookbooks or online for ideas.

Notes:_____

_____

_____

_____

_____

_____

SINCE 1991

BAKERY

• PREMIUM GOODS •

Coconut Dream Pie

Ingredients

- 1 cup sweetened flaked coconut

- 3 cups half-and-half

- 2 eggs, beaten

- 3/4 cup granulated sugar

- 1/2 cup all-purpose flour

- 1/4 tsp salt

- 1 1/2 tsp vanilla extract.

- 1 - 9 inch pie shell, baked (or any pre-made crust you like)

- 1 cup frozen whipped topping, thawed

Instructions

Preheat oven to 350°F.
Spread the coconut on a baking sheet and bake it, stirring occasionally, until golden brown, about 5 minutes.
In a medium saucepan, combine the half-and-half, eggs, sugar, flour, and salt and mix well.
Bring to a boil over low heat, stirring constantly.
Remove the pan from the heat and stir in 3/4 cup of the toasted coconut and vanilla extract.
Reserve the remaining coconut to top the pie.
Pour the filling into the pie shell and chill until firm, about 4 hours.
Top with whipped topping and reserved coconut.
Share with family and friends!

How many stars do you give this recipe?

Baking Time!

Notes:_____

_____

_____

_____

_____

_____

Draw a picture of
your baking creation!

Plans & Priorities

Date:_____

To-do List:
_____
_____
_____
_____
_____

A Quote:
_____
_____
_____
_____

Shopping List:
_____
_____
_____
_____

My Plans:
_____
_____
_____
_____

I am Thankful for:

_____
_____
_____
_____

Relax & Be Creative

Baking Challenge

Make doughnut holes! Try a few different coatings: vanilla glaze, cinnamon sugar, sprinkles, or chocolate dip.

Draw what you've made!

How many stars do you give your work?

Notes:_____

Reading Time!

Choose a few books from your stack
to focus on today. Write down or draw
anything that inspires you.

Screen Time

Watch a cooking show, high-quality film, video, documentary, or baking tutorial.

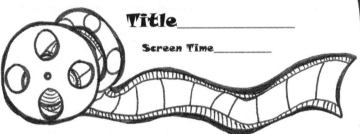

Title_____

Screen Time_____

Notes

Take notes on what you are learning.

_____
_____
_____
_____
_____
_____
_____

Rating:

Worst

Bad

Awful

Ok

Nice

Great

Best

Math Practice

Use this page for math practice, graphic design, and creative measurements. If you have a book on mathematics use this page for notes.

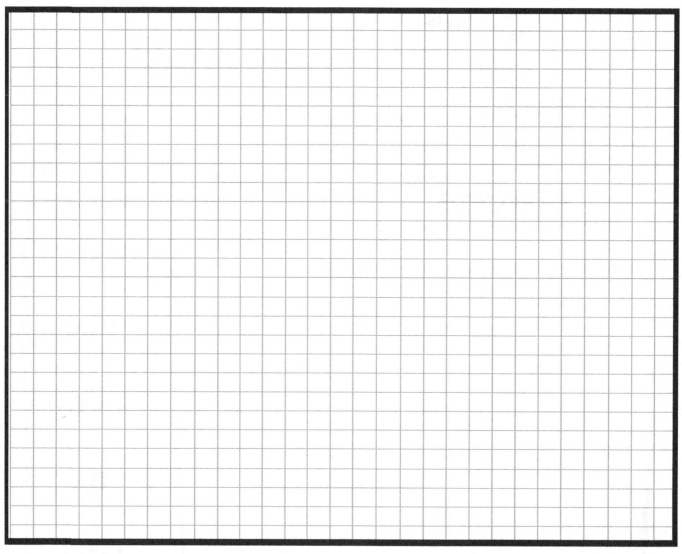

Notes:_____
_____
_____
_____
_____
_____
_____
_____

Baking Dreams

Design something beautiful you want to bake!

Look at photos in your cookbooks or online for ideas.

Notes:_____

_____

_____

_____

_____

_____

SINCE 1991

BAKERY

• PREMIUM GOODS •

No-Bake Key Lime Cheesecake

Ingredients

Crust
- 2 1/2 cups graham cracker cookies, crushed

- 1/2 cup / 1 stick of unsalted butter, melted

Pie filling
- 1 1/4 cup full-fat cream cheese, room temperature

- 1 cup sweetened condensed milk

- 1/2 cup lime juice, freshly squeezed

- 1 cup thickened or heavy cream

- 1 tsp vanilla extract

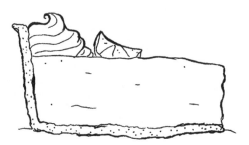

Topping
- 1 cup whipped cream or whipped topping

- lime zest, to decorate

Instructions
Add cookies to a food processor or blender and blend until finely crushed.
Add melted butter and mix well.
Pour crumbs into a 9-inch pie plate.
Press down firmly to form a crust and place in the fridge.
Put the cream cheese in a large mixing bowl.
Use an electric mixer to beat until smooth.
Add condensed milk and lime juice and beat briefly until combined.
Finally, add the cream and beat for 2-3 minutes,
until mixture is thick and creamy.
Pour lime mixture over crust and smooth top.
Place in the fridge for 6 hours, or even better, overnight.
Place cream in a large bowl and beat with an electric mixer until cream is whipped.
Cover key lime pie with cream. Scatter over lime zest.
Cut, serve and enjoy!

How many stars do you give this recipe?

Baking Time!

Notes: _____

_____

_____

_____

_____

**Draw a picture of
your baking creation!**

Plans & Priorities

Date:_____

To-do List:
_____
_____
_____
_____
_____

A Quote:
_____
_____
_____
_____
_____

Shopping List:
_____
_____
_____
_____
_____

My Plans:
_____
_____
_____
_____

I am Thankful for:

_____
_____
_____
_____

Baking Challenge

Research and make a French dessert.

Draw what you've made!

How many stars do you give your work?

Notes:_____

Reading Time!

Choose a few books from your stack to focus on today. Write down or draw anything that inspires you.

Screen Time

Watch a cooking show, high-quality film, video, documentary, or baking tutorial.

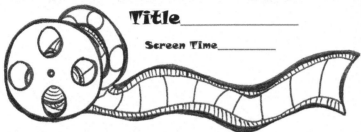

Title_____

Screen Time_____

Notes

Take notes on what you are learning.

_____

_____

_____

_____

_____

_____

_____

Rating:

Worst

Bad

Awful

Ok

Nice

Great

Best

Math Practice

Use this page for math practice, graphic design, and creative measurements. If you have a book on mathematics use this page for notes.

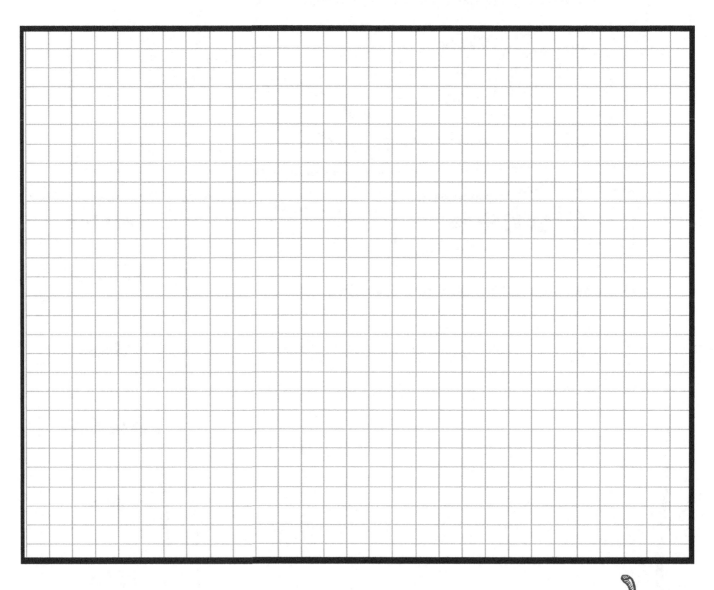

Notes:_____

_____

_____

_____

_____

_____

_____

Baking Dreams

Design something beautiful you want to bake!

Look at photos in your cookbooks or online for ideas.

Notes: _____

_____

_____

_____

_____

_____

SINCE 1991

BAKERY

• PREMIUM GOODS •

Mango Nice Cream

Ingredients

- 2 frozen bananas

- 1 cup of frozen mango

- 2 tbsp heavy cream or coconut cream

Instructions

Blend everything together in a blender
or food processor and serve.

How many stars do you give this recipe?

Baking Time!

Notes:_____
_____
_____
_____
_____
_____

Draw a picture of
your baking creation!

Plans & Priorities

Date:_____

To-do List:
_____
_____
_____
_____

A Quote:
_____
_____
_____
_____

Shopping List:
_____
_____
_____
_____

My Plans:
_____
_____
_____

I am Thankful for:
_____
_____
_____
_____

Relax & Be Creative

Baking Challenge

Research and make a paleo dessert.

Draw what you've made!

How many stars do you give your work?

Notes:_____

Reading Time!

Choose a few books from your stack to focus on today. Write down or draw anything that inspires you.

Screen Time

Watch a cooking show, high-quality film, video, documentary, or baking tutorial.

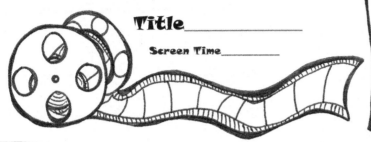

Title_____

Screen Time_____

Notes

Take notes on what you are learning.

_____
_____
_____
_____
_____
_____
_____

Rating:

Worst

Bad

Awful

Ok

Nice

Great

Best

Math Practice

Use this page for math practice, graphic design, and creative measurements. If you have a book on mathematics use this page for notes.

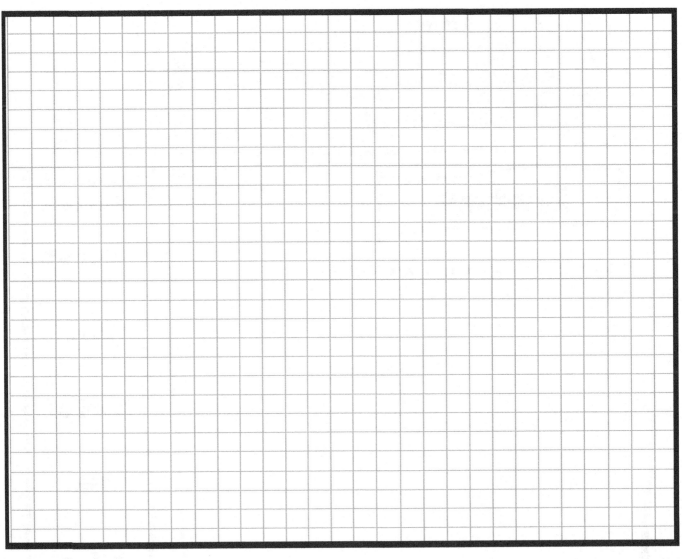

Notes:_____
_____
_____
_____
_____
_____
_____
_____

Baking Dreams

Design something beautiful you want to bake!

Look at photos in your cookbooks or online for ideas.

Notes:_____

_____

_____

_____

_____

_____

_____

SINCE 1991

BAKERY

• PREMIUM GOODS •

Chocolate Cake in a Mug

Ingredients
1/4 cup all-purpose flour

2 tbsp unsweetened cocoa powder

1/4 tsp baking powder

2 tbsp granulated sugar
(you can add 1 tbsp more if you like it a bit sweeter)

1/8 tsp salt

1/4 cup + 1 tbsp milk

2 tbsp vegetable oil

1 tbsp Nutella or mini chocolate chips

Instructions
In a medium bowl, whisk together dry ingredients.
Whisk in the milk and vegetable oil until all ingredients
are combined and batter has no clumps.
Pour batter into a microwave-safe mug (Mine was a 14-ounce mug).
You want enough space for the cake to rise without pouring over.
Add Nutella or mini chocolate chips into the middle of the batter.
Drop it in the middle, no need to push it down and sink it in the
batter. It does that on its own when it cooks!
Place a paper towel into the microwave and set the mug on top
(this is to catch any batter if your mug cake overflows).
Microwave mug cake for 70 seconds on high.
Top with whipped cream or ice cream and eat warm.

How many stars do you give this recipe?

Baking Time!

Notes:
_____
_____
_____
_____
_____
_____

Draw a picture of your baking creation!

Plans & Priorities

Date: _____

To-do List:
_____
_____
_____
_____

A Quote:
_____
_____
_____
_____

Shopping List:
_____
_____
_____
_____

My Plans:
_____
_____
_____
_____

I am Thankful for:
_____
_____
_____
_____

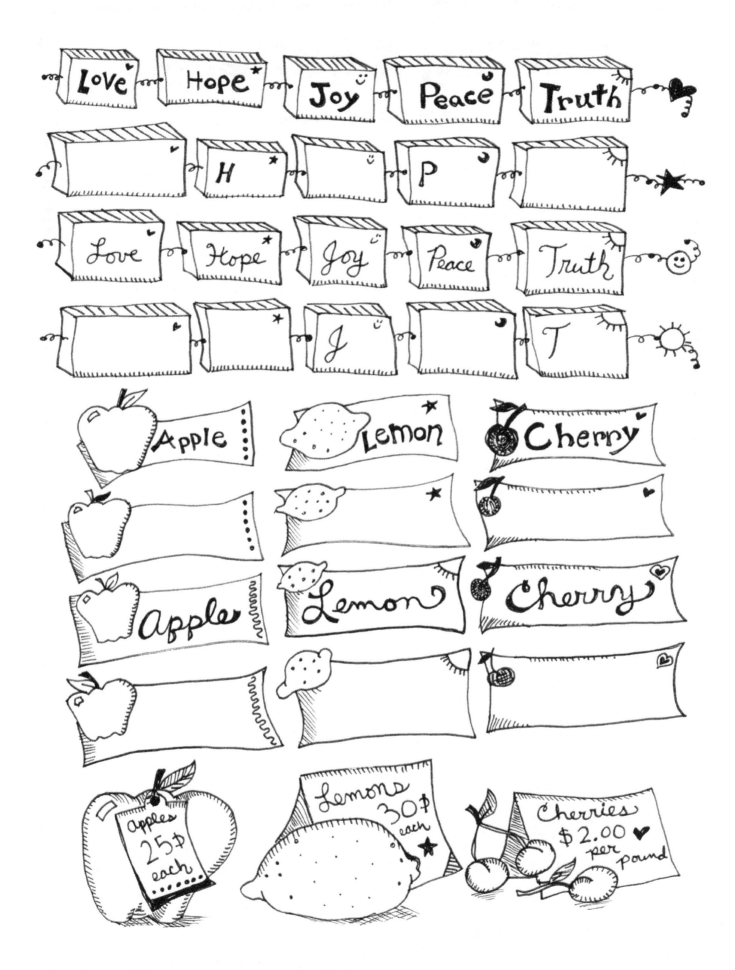

Baking Challenge

Make challah bread.

Draw what you've made!

How many stars do you give your work?

Notes:_____

Reading Time!

Choose a few books from your stack to focus on today. Write down or draw anything that inspires you.

Screen Time

Watch a cooking show, high-quality film, video, documentary, or baking tutorial.

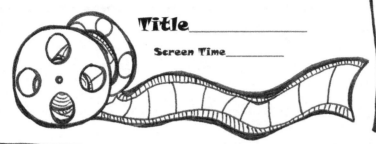

Title_____

Screen Time_____

Notes

Take notes on what you are learning.

_____

_____

_____

_____

_____

_____

_____

Rating:

Worst

Bad

Awful

Ok

Nice

Great

Best

Math Practice

Use this page for math practice, graphic design, and creative measurements. If you have a book on mathematics use this page for notes.

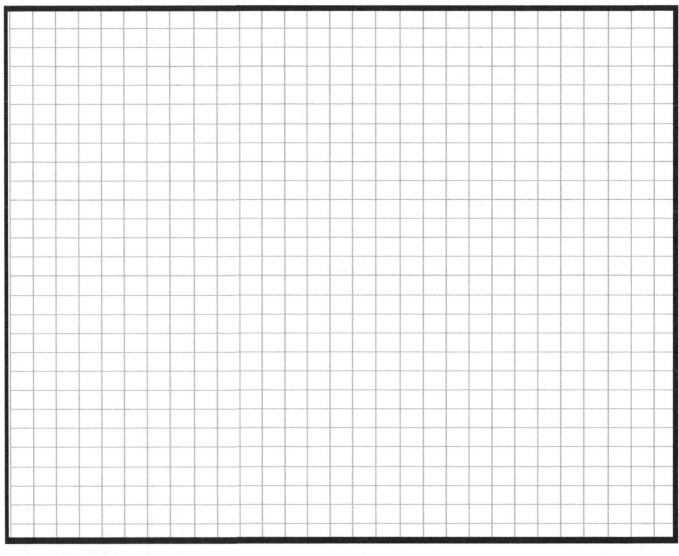

Notes:_____

_____

_____

_____

_____

_____

_____

Baking Dreams

Design something beautiful you want to bake!

Look at photos in your cookbooks or online for ideas.

Notes:_____

_____

_____

_____

_____

_____

SINCE 1991

BAKERY

• PREMIUM GOODS •

Strawberry Nice Cream

Ingredients

- 2 frozen bananas

- 1 cup of frozen strawberries

- 2 tbsp heavy cream or coconut cream

Instructions

Blend everything together in a blender
or food processor and serve.

How many stars do you give this recipe?

Baking Time!

Notes: _____
_____
_____
_____
_____
_____

Draw a picture of your baking creation!

Plans & Priorities

Date:_____

To-do List:
_____
_____
_____
_____

A Quote:
_____
_____
_____
_____

Shopping List:
_____
_____
_____
_____

My Plans:
_____
_____
_____
_____

I am Thankful for:

_____
_____
_____
_____

Relax & Be Creative

Baking Challenge

Research and make a sugar-free dessert.

Draw what you've made!

How many stars do you give your work?

Notes:_____

Reading Time!

Choose a few books from your stack to focus on today. Write down or draw anything that inspires you.

Screen Time

Watch a cooking show, high-quality film, video, documentary, or baking tutorial.

Title_____

Screen Time_____

Notes

Take notes on what you are learning.

_____

_____

_____

_____

_____

_____

_____

Rating:

Worst

Bad

Awful

Ok

Nice

Great

Best

Math Practice

Use this page for math practice, graphic design, and creative measurements. If you have a book on mathematics use this page for notes.

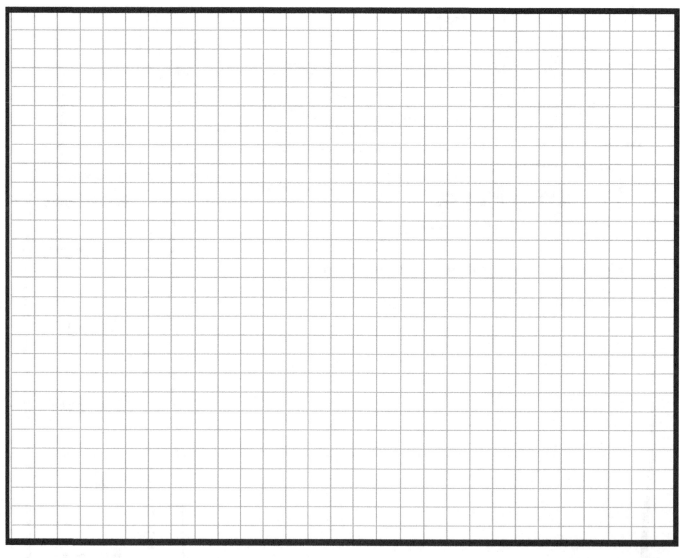

Notes:_____

_____

_____

_____

_____

_____

_____

_____

Baking Dreams

Design something beautiful you want to bake!

Look at photos in your cookbooks or online for ideas.

Notes:_____

_____

_____

_____

_____

_____

_____

SINCE 1991

BAKERY

• PREMIUM GOODS •

The Best Apple Crisp

Ingredients

Apple filling

- 6-8 medium apples, peeled and sliced into wedges
- 1/4 tsp salt
- 3/4 cup sugar
- 2 tsp cinnamon

Crisp topping

- 1 cup brown sugar
- 1 cup rolled oats
- 1/2 cup all-purpose flour
- 1/2 cup unsalted butter, melted

Instructions

Preheat oven to 350°F.

In a large mixing bowl combine salt, sugar, and cinnamon.

Add sliced apples into sugar/cinnamon mixture
and toss until well-coated.

Pour coated apples into a medium-sized baking dish.

In a separate bowl, combine brown sugar, oats,
flour, and melted butter until crumbly.

Spread the crumble topping evenly over apples.

Bake at 350 for 30 minutes until bubbly and golden.

How many stars do you give this recipe?

Baking Time!

Notes:_____

_____

_____

_____

_____

_____

**Draw a picture of
your baking creation!**

Plans & Priorities

Date:_____

To-do List:
_____
_____
_____
_____

A Quote:
_____
_____
_____
_____

Shopping List:
_____
_____
_____
_____
_____

My Plans:
_____
_____
_____
_____

I am Thankful for:
_____
_____
_____
_____

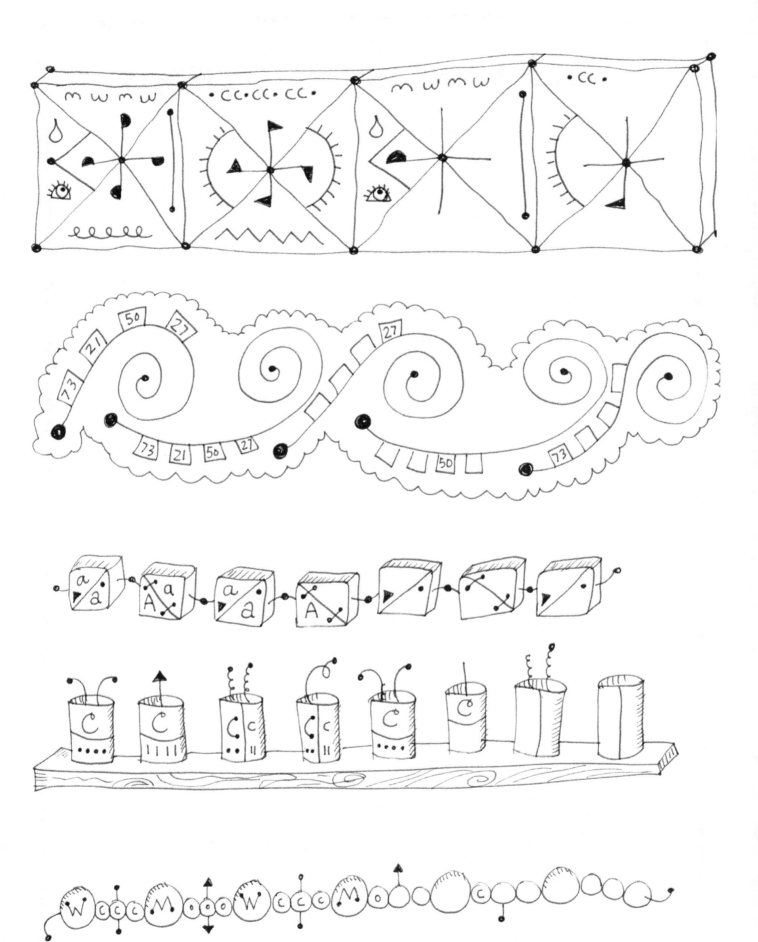

Baking Challenge

Make buttery croissants.

Draw what you've made!

How many stars do you give your work?

Notes:_____

Reading Time!

Choose a few books from your stack
to focus on today. Write down or draw
anything that inspires you.

Screen Time

Watch a cooking show, high-quality film, video, documentary, or baking tutorial.

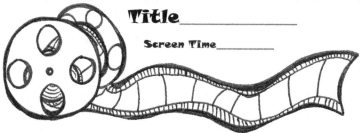

Title_____

Screen Time_____

Notes

Take notes on what you are learning.

_____
_____
_____
_____
_____
_____
_____

Rating:

Worst

Bad

Awful

Ok

Nice

Great

Best

Math Practice

Use this page for math practice, graphic design, and creative measurements. If you have a book on mathematics use this page for notes.

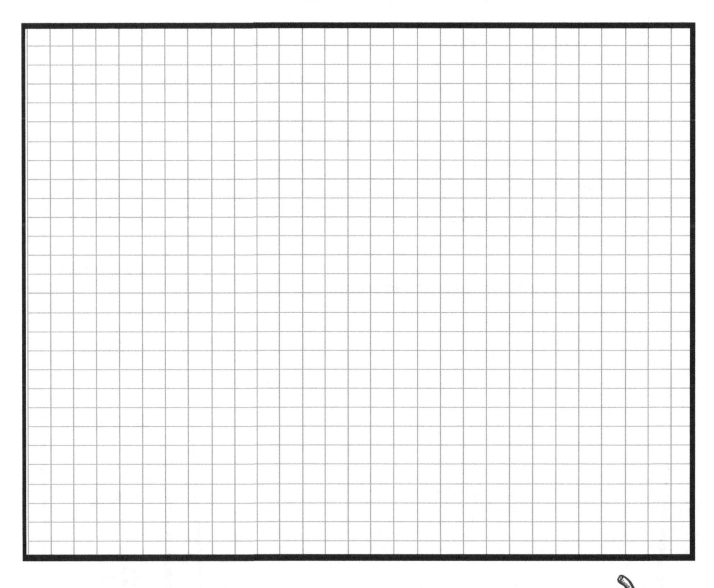

Notes:_____
_____
_____
_____
_____
_____
_____
_____

Baking Dreams

Design something beautiful you want to bake!

Look at photos in your cookbooks or online for ideas.

Notes:_____

_____

_____

_____

_____

_____

SINCE   1991

BAKERY

• PREMIUM GOODS •

Chocolate Peanut Butter Nice Cream

Ingredients
- 2 frozen bananas

- 1 tbsp coco powder

- 2 tbsp peanut butter

- 2 tbsp heavy cream or coconut cream

Instructions
Blend everything together in a
blender or food processor and serve.

How many stars do you give this recipe?

Baking Time!

Notes: _____

_____

_____

_____

_____

_____

Draw a picture of your baking creation!

Plans & Priorities

Date:_____

To-do List:
_____
_____
_____
_____
_____

A Quote:
_____
_____
_____
_____
_____

Shopping List:
_____
_____
_____
_____
_____

My Plans:
_____
_____
_____
_____

I am Thankful for:
_____
_____
_____
_____

Baking Challenge

Make stuffed french toast. You could do strawberry cheesecake, Nutella cream banana, or cream cheese apple pie. Be creative and make your family happy they bought you this book!

Draw what you've made!

How many stars do you give your work?

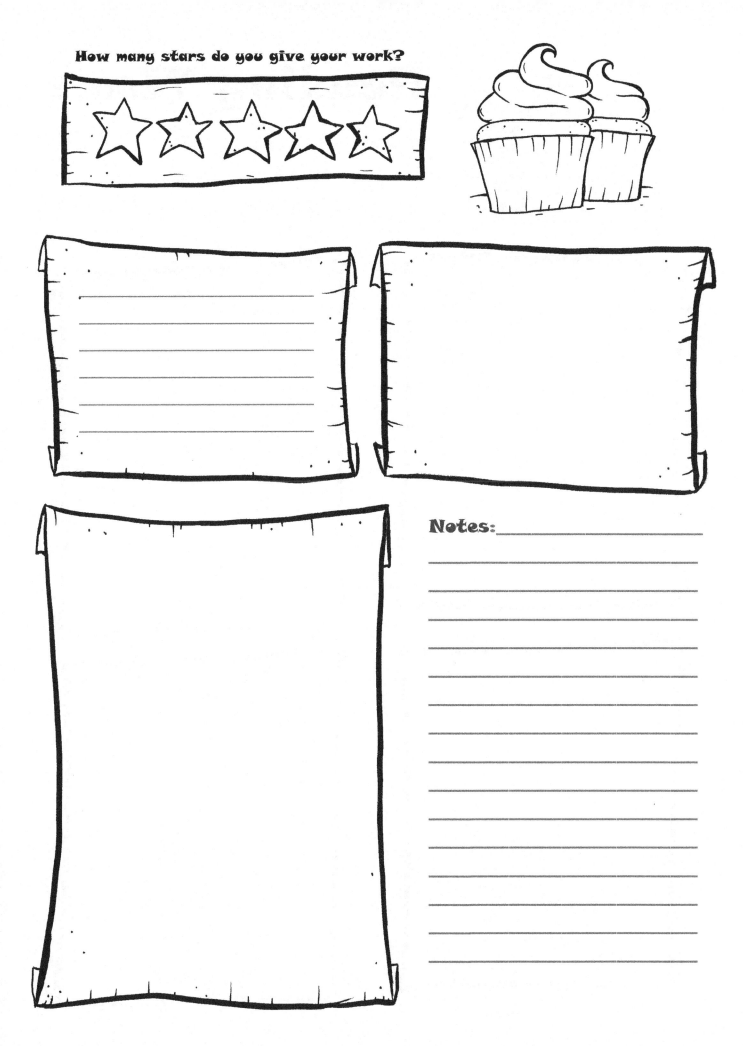

Notes:_____

Reading Time!

Choose a few books from your stack to focus on today. Write down or draw anything that inspires you.

Screen Time

Watch a cooking show, high-quality film, video, documentary, or baking tutorial.

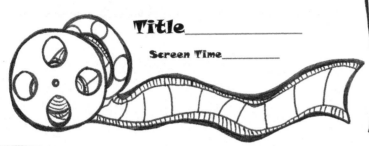

Title_____

Screen Time_____

Notes

Take notes on what you are learning.

_____

_____

_____

_____

_____

_____

_____

Rating:

Worst

Bad

Awful

Ok

Nice

Great

Best

Math Practice

Use this page for math practice, graphic design, and creative measurements. If you have a book on mathematics use this page for notes.

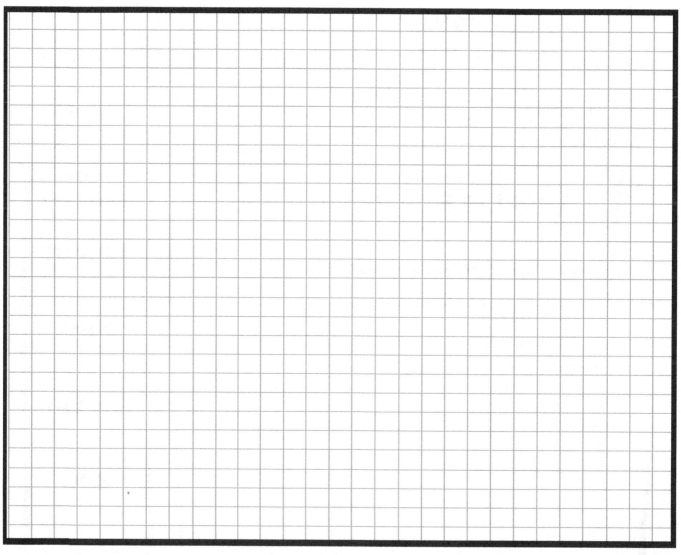

Notes:_____

_____

_____

_____

_____

_____

_____

Baking Dreams

Design something beautiful you want to bake!

Look at photos in your cookbooks or online for ideas.

Notes:_____

_____

_____

_____

_____

_____

SINCE 1991
BAKERY
• PREMIUM GOODS •

Double Chocolate Chewy Brownies

Ingredients

- 1 cup butter
- 1 cup white granulated sugar
- 1 cup brown sugar
- 2/3 cup cocoa
- 3 eggs
- 1 cup all-purpose flour
- 1 1/2 tsp baking powder
- 1 1/2 tsp vanilla extract

Instructions

Preheat oven to 350°F.
Melt butter in a large pot over low heat.
Once melted, remove from heat.
Add both white and brown sugar, and cocoa.
Mix with a wooden spoon.
In a separate bowl, beat three eggs. Add eggs to butter/sugar mixture. Mix well with a whisk.
Sift flour and baking powder over the mixture and stir in.
Add vanilla and mix.
Pour into a lightly greased 9 x 11 baking pan.
Bake for 25 minutes. Let cool for 15 minutes.

How many stars do you give this recipe?

Baking Time!

Notes:_____

_____

_____

_____

_____

_____

**Draw a picture of
your baking creation!**

Plans & Priorities

Date:_____

To-do List:
_____
_____
_____
_____

A Quote:
_____
_____
_____
_____

Shopping List:
_____
_____
_____
_____

My Plans:
_____
_____
_____
_____

I am Thankful for:
_____
_____
_____
_____

Baking Challenge

Make fudge. Be creative with the flavor!
My favorite is peanut butter.

Draw what you've made!

How many stars do you give your work?

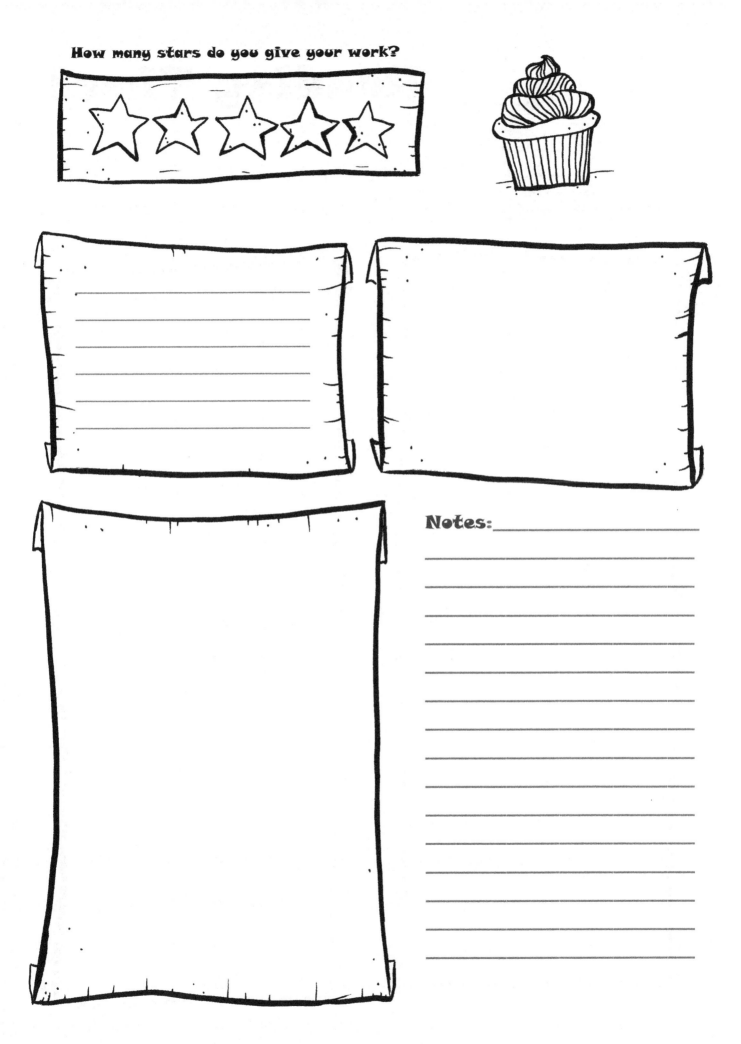

Notes:_____

Reading Time!

Choose a few books from your stack to focus on today. Write down or draw anything that inspires you.

Screen Time

Watch a cooking show, high-quality film, video, documentary, or baking tutorial.

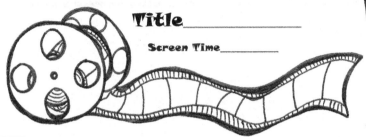

Title_____

Screen Time_____

Notes

Take notes on what you are learning.

_____

_____

_____

_____

_____

_____

_____

Rating:

Worst

Bad

Awful

Ok

Nice

Great

Best

Math Practice

Use this page for math practice, graphic design, and creative measurements. If you have a book on mathematics use this page for notes.

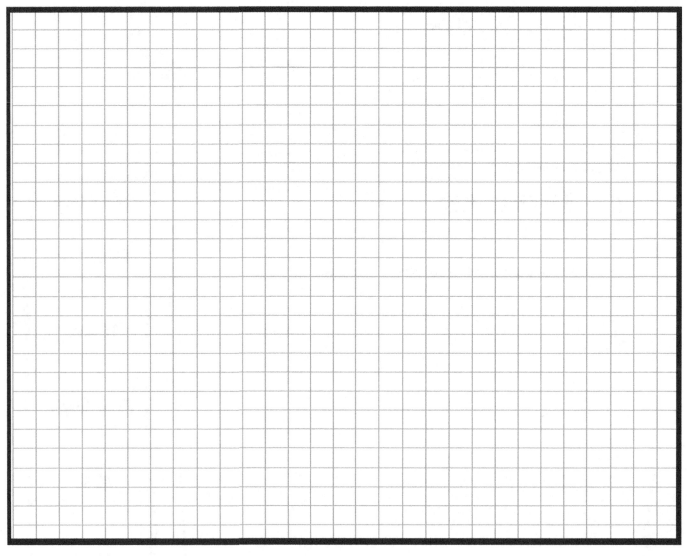

Notes:_____

_____

_____

_____

_____

_____

_____

_____

Baking Dreams

Design something beautiful you want to bake!

Look at photos in your cookbooks or online for ideas.

Notes:_____

_____

_____

_____

_____

_____

SINCE 1991

BAKERY

• PREMIUM GOODS •

Superfood Nice Cream

Ingredients
- 2 frozen bananas

- 1/2 cup of frozen mango or pineapple

- 1/4 cup blueberries

- A handful of kale

- A tsp of chia seeds

- 2 tbsp heavy cream or coconut cream

Instructions
Blend everything together in a blender or food processor and serve.

How many stars do you give this recipe?

Baking Time!

Notes: _____

_____

_____

_____

_____

_____

Draw a picture of your baking creation!

Plans & Priorities

Date:_____

To-do List:
_____
_____
_____
_____
_____

A Quote:
_____
_____
_____
_____
_____

Shopping List:
_____
_____
_____
_____
_____

My Plans:
_____
_____
_____
_____

I am Thankful for:
_____
_____
_____
_____

Relax & Be Creative

Baking Challenge

Make a pancake cake.
This is where you make about 20 pancakes and then layer them
with strawberries and sweetened cream cheese.
It's your call if you want to frost the whole
cake or leave it with the raw look.
You can top the cake with strawberries
and drizzle with maple syrup.

Draw what you've made!

How many stars do you give your work?

Notes:_____

Reading Time!

Choose a few books from your stack to focus on today. Write down or draw anything that inspires you.

Screen Time

Watch a cooking show, high-quality film, video, documentary, or baking tutorial.

Title_____

Screen Time_____

Notes

Take notes on what you are learning.

_____

_____

_____

_____

_____

_____

Rating:

Worst

Bad

Awful

Ok

Nice

Great

Best

Math Practice

Use this page for math practice, graphic design, and creative measurements. If you have a book on mathematics use this page for notes.

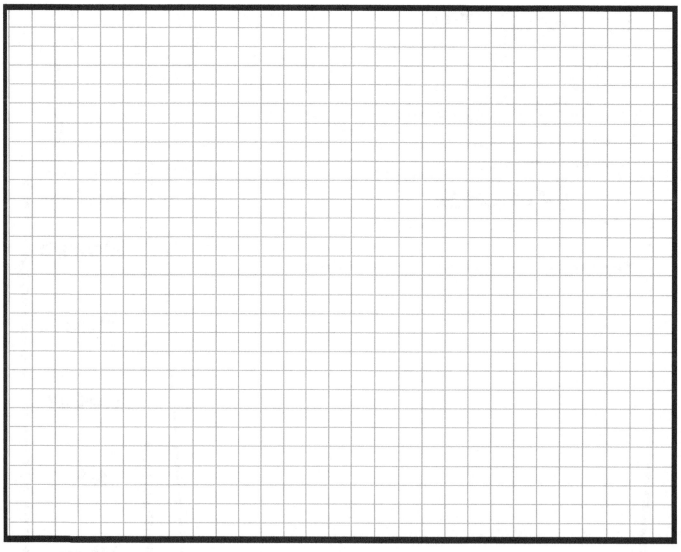

Notes:_____

_____

_____

_____

_____

_____

_____

_____

Baking Dreams

Design something beautiful you want to bake!

Look at photos in your cookbooks or online for ideas.

Notes:_____

_____

_____

_____

_____

_____

SINCE 1991

BAKERY

• PREMIUM GOODS •

World's Best Lemon Bars

Ingredients

Base
- 1 cup of all-purpose flour
- 1/2 cup butter, softened
- 1/3 cup white sugar

Lemon topping
- 1 cup of white sugar
- 2 beaten eggs
- 1 tbsp finely grated lemon zest
- 3 tbsp freshly squeezed lemon juice ~ 1 lemon
- 2 tbsp all-purpose flour
- 1 tsp vanilla
- 1/2 tsp baking powder
- 1/4 tsp salt

Instructions
Preheat oven to 325°F.
In a food processor (or by hand) pulse flour, sugar,
and butter (cubed) until combined.
The mixture will resemble coarse crumbs.
Press firmly into a 8" x 8" baking dish.
Bake at 325 for 20 minutes.
In a medium-sized mixing bowl, combine sugar, vanilla, beaten eggs, lemon zest,
juice, flour, baking powder, and salt with a whisk until well combined.

How many stars do you give this recipe?

Baking Time!

Notes: _____

_____

_____

_____

_____

_____

Draw a picture of your baking creation!

Plans & Priorities

Date:_____

To-do List:

_____
_____
_____
_____
_____

A Quote:

_____
_____
_____
_____

Shopping List:

_____
_____
_____
_____

My Plans:

_____
_____
_____
_____

I am Thankful for:

_____
_____
_____
_____

Baking Challenge

Make something delicious using only 3 ingredients.

Draw what you've made!

How many stars do you give your work?

Notes:_____

Reading Time!

Choose a few books from your stack to focus on today. Write down or draw anything that inspires you.

Screen Time

Watch a cooking show, high-quality film, video, documentary, or baking tutorial.

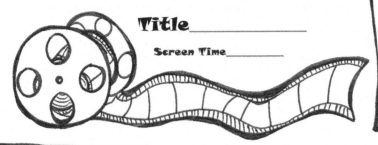

Title_____

Screen Time_____

Notes

Take notes on what you are learning.

_____
_____
_____
_____
_____
_____
_____

Rating:

Worst

Bad

Awful

Ok

Nice

Great

Best

Math Practice

Use this page for math practice, graphic design, and creative measurements. If you have a book on mathematics use this page for notes.

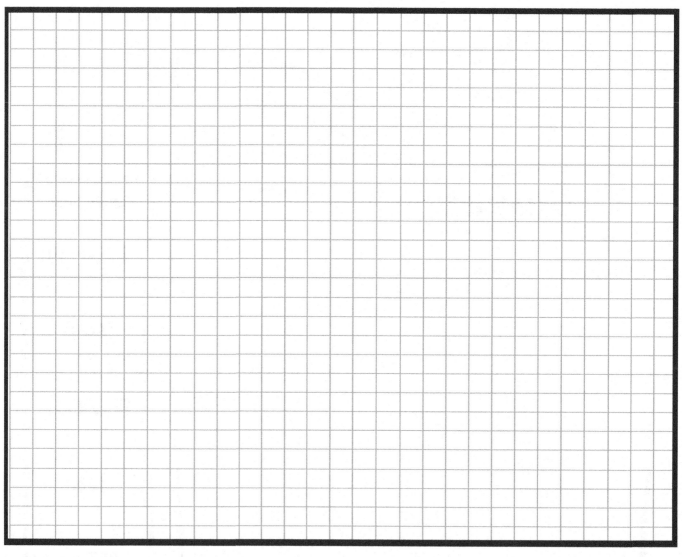

Notes:_____

_____

_____

_____

_____

_____

_____

_____

Baking Dreams

Design something beautiful you want to bake!

Look at photos in your cookbooks or online for ideas.

Notes:_____

_____

_____

_____

_____

_____

SINCE 1991

BAKERY

• PREMIUM GOODS •

Raspberry Cheesecake Nice Cream

Ingredients
- 2 frozen bananas

- ½ cup of raspberries

- 2 tbsp cream cheese

- 2 tbsp heavy cream

- A crushed graham cracker crust

Instructions
Blend everything together except cream cheese in a blender or food processor.
After all is blended well, add cream cheese, but only blend for a second.
The goal is to not blend in the cream cheese, but keep it in streaks.
Scoop into bowl and sprinkle with the crumbled graham cracker.

How many stars do you give this recipe?

Baking Time!

Notes: _____

_____

_____

_____

_____

_____

**Draw a picture of
your baking creation!**

Plans & Priorities

Date:_____

To-do List:
_____
_____
_____
_____

A Quote:
_____
_____
_____
_____

Shopping List:
_____
_____
_____
_____

My Plans:
_____
_____
_____
_____

I am Thankful for:
_____
_____
_____
_____

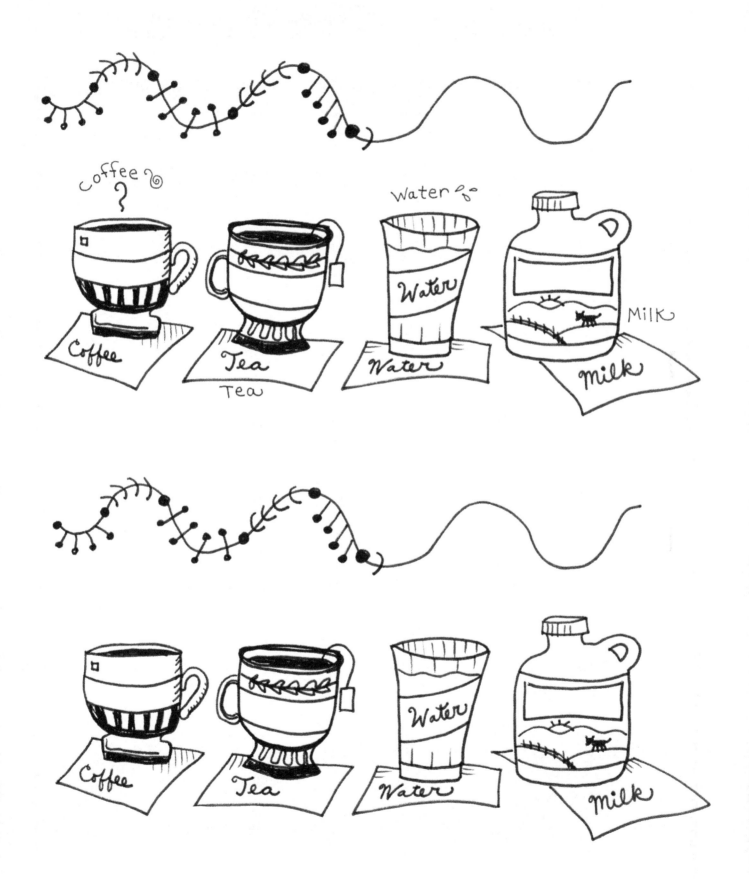

Baking Challenge

Make those chocolate peanut butter no-bakes like the aunties always bring around Christmas-time.

Draw what you've made!

How many stars do you give your work?

Notes:

Reading Time!

Choose a few books from your stack to focus on today. Write down or draw anything that inspires you.

Screen Time

Watch a cooking show, high-quality film, video, documentary, or baking tutorial.

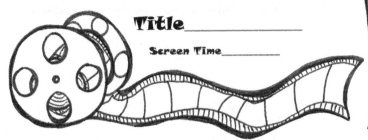

Title_____

Screen Time_____

Notes

Take notes on what you are learning.

_____
_____
_____
_____
_____
_____
_____

Rating:

Worst

Bad

Awful

Ok

Nice

Great

Best

Math Practice

Use this page for math practice, graphic design, and creative measurements. If you have a book on mathematics use this page for notes.

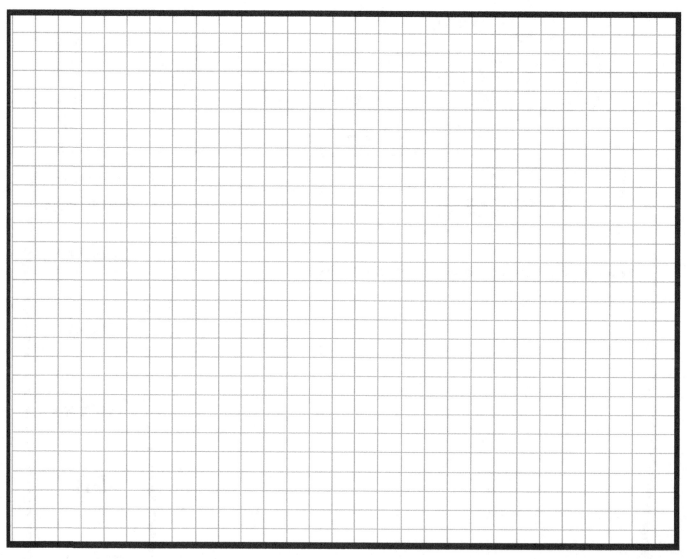

Notes:_____

_____

_____

_____

_____

_____

_____

_____

_____

Baking Dreams

Design something beautiful you want to bake!

Look at photos in your cookbooks or online for ideas.

Notes:_____

_____

_____

_____

_____

_____

SINCE   1991

BAKERY

• PREMIUM GOODS •

Chewy Chocolate Oat Cookies

Ingredients

- 2 cups white sugar

- 1/2 cup butter

- 1/2 cup milk

- 6 tbsp cocoa powder

- 1 cup shredded coconut (sweetened)

- 3 cups quick oats

- 1/2 tsp salt

- 1 1/2 tsp vanilla

Instructions

In a large stovetop/broiler pot, whisk sugar, butter, milk, and cocoa powder—bring to a boil over medium heat. Remove from heat and cool slightly (10 minutes—no longer!). Once cool, stir in salt and vanilla, followed by the quick oats and sweetened, shredded coconut. Spoon onto wax paper (approximately 1 heaping tablespoon per cookie) and let set for one hour before freezing or serving.

Makes 30-36 chocolate cookies, depending on the size of your spoonfuls.

How many stars do you give this recipe?

Baking Time!

Notes:_____

_____

_____

_____

_____

_____

Draw a picture of your baking creation!

Plans & Priorities

Date:_____

To-do List:
_____
_____
_____
_____
_____

A Quote:
_____
_____
_____
_____

Shopping List:
_____
_____
_____
_____

My Plans:
_____
_____
_____

I am Thankful for:
_____
_____
_____
_____

Relax & Be Creative

Baking Challenge

Research and make a keto dessert.

Draw what you've made!

How many stars do you give your work?

Notes:_____

Reading Time!

Choose a few books from your stack to focus on today. Write down or draw anything that inspires you.

Screen Time

Watch a cooking show, high-quality film, video, documentary, or baking tutorial.

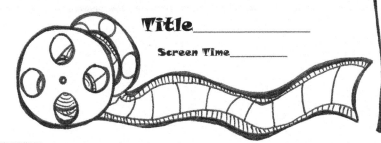

Title_____

Screen Time_____

Notes

Take notes on what you are learning.

_____
_____
_____
_____
_____
_____
_____

Rating:

Worst

Bad

Awful

Ok

Nice

Great

Best

Math Practice

Use this page for math practice, graphic design, and creative measurements. If you have a book on mathematics use this page for notes.

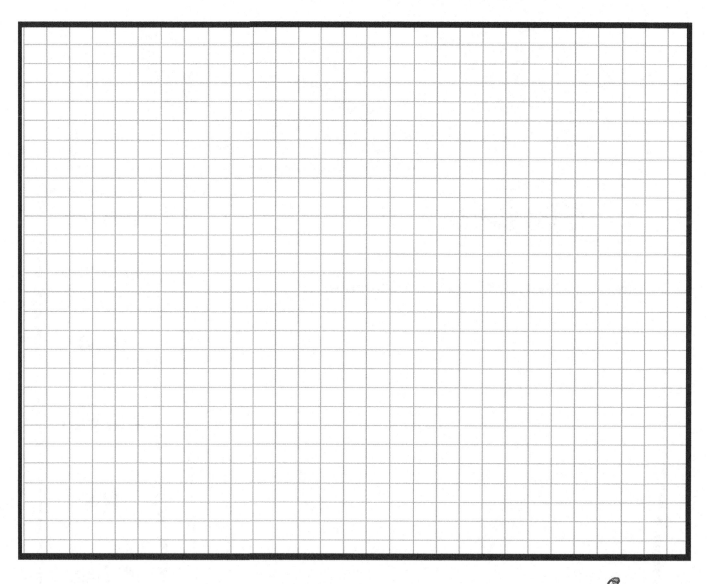

Notes:_____
_____
_____
_____
_____
_____
_____
_____

Baking Dreams

Design something beautiful you want to bake!

Look at photos in your cookbooks or online for ideas.

Notes:_____

_____

_____

_____

_____

_____

SINCE   1991

BAKERY
• PREMIUM GOODS •

Crisp and Chewy Ginger Snappers

Ingredients

- 3/4 cup butter

- 1 cup white sugar (and extra sugar for rolling balls)

- 4 tbsp molasses

- 1 egg

- 1 tsp salt

- 2 cups all-purpose flour

- 2 tsp baking soda

- 1 1/2 tsp cinnamon

- 1 tsp cloves

- 1 tsp ground ginger

Instructions

Preheat oven to 350°F.
Cream butter with sugar and molasses.
Add egg and dry ingredients.
Mix together and roll into walnut-size balls.
Roll in sugar. No need to flatten; they'll do that on their own.
Bake for 8-10 minutes at 375. Makes 32-36 cookies.

How many stars do you give this recipe?

Baking Time!

Notes: _____

_____

_____

_____

_____

_____

**Draw a picture of
your baking creation!**

Plans & Priorities

Date:_____

To-do List:
_____
_____
_____
_____

A Quote:
_____
_____
_____
_____

Shopping List:
_____
_____
_____
_____

My Plans:
_____
_____
_____
_____

I am Thankful for:

_____
_____
_____
_____

DESIGN MENUS FOR YOUR BAKERY

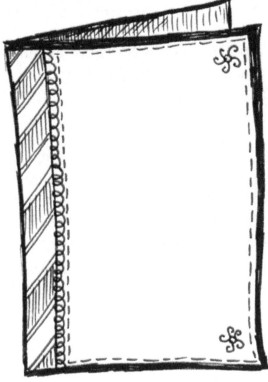

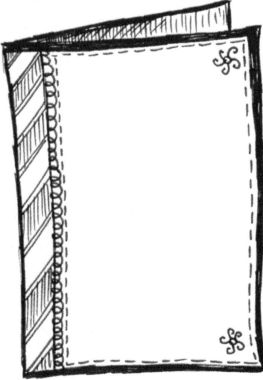

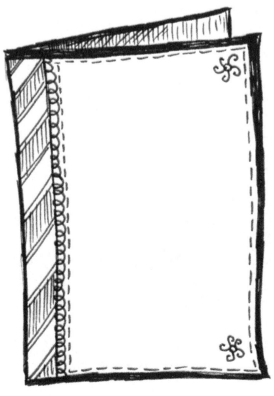

Baking Challenge

Make a no-bake layered cream pie. Everyone needs to know how to make one of these. You can be creative, but the basics are:

One layer is a pudding/cream cheese base.

Another layer is only pudding and the last layer is a dollop of whipped cream. You could do a strawberry-cheesecake style pie, peanut butter chocolate or maybe cookie dough. My favorite is the cookies and cream pie.

First you use a graham cracker crust. Then you crush Oreos and mix them into your whipped pudding/cream cheese, If you want it sweeter add sugar. Then smooth it down on the pie crust. Next, scoop on chocolate pudding and gently even it out. Then you pile on your homemade whipped cream or store bought whipped topping. Finish the dessert by sprinkling crumbled Oreos on top.

If you want some extra pizazz, drizzle on some chocolate syrup.

Draw what you've made!

How many stars do you give your work?

Notes:

Reading Time!

Choose a few books from your stack to focus on today. Write down or draw anything that inspires you.

Screen Time

Watch a cooking show, high-quality film, video, documentary, or baking tutorial.

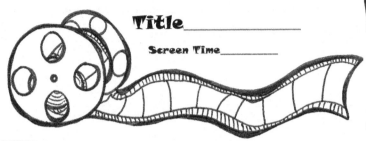

Title_____

Screen Time_____

Notes

Take notes on what you are learning.

_____
_____
_____
_____
_____
_____
_____

Rating:

Worst

Bad

Awful

Ok

Nice

Great

Best

Math Practice

Use this page for math practice, graphic design, and creative measurements. If you have a book on mathematics use this page for notes.

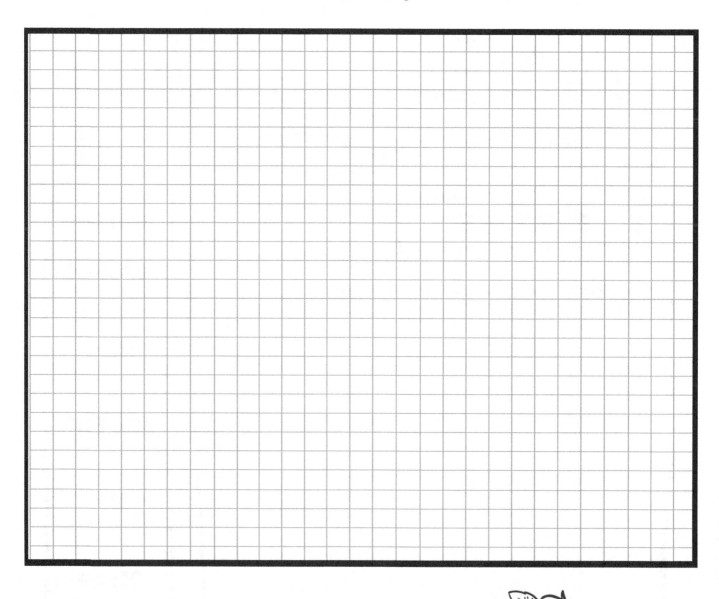

Notes:_____
_____
_____
_____
_____
_____
_____

Baking Dreams

Design something beautiful you want to bake!

Look at photos in your cookbooks or online for ideas.

Notes:_____

_____

_____

_____

_____

SINCE 1991

BAKERY

• PREMIUM GOODS •

Chewy Oatmeal Cookies

Ingredients

- 1 cup butter, softened
- 2 cups brown sugar
- 2 eggs
- 1 1/2 tsp vanilla
- 2 cups large rolled oats or quick oats
- 1 cup shredded sweetened, coconut
- 2 cups all-purpose flour
- 1/2 tsp baking soda
- 1 tsp salt

Instructions

Preheat oven to 350°F.

In a large mixing bowl, cream butter and brown sugar.

Mix in eggs and vanilla.

In a separate bowl, combine oats, shredded coconut, flour, baking soda, and salt.

Add oat mixture to the wet ingredients and mix until well combined.

Using a cookie scoop or spoon, form dough into 2 teaspoon-sized balls and flatten them using your fingers or a fork. They don't spread out much, so be sure to flatten them.

Place on a cookie sheet and bake at 375 for 8-10 minutes, until golden. Serve and enjoy!

How many stars do you give this recipe?

Baking Time!

Notes: _____

_____

_____

_____

_____

_____

Draw a picture of
your baking creation!

Plans & Priorities

Date:_____

To-do List:

_____
_____
_____
_____
_____

A Quote:

_____
_____
_____
_____

Shopping List:

_____
_____
_____
_____
_____

My Plans:

_____
_____
_____
_____

I am Thankful for:

_____
_____
_____
_____

Baking Challenge

Mix two desserts together. Be creative.

Draw what you've made!

How many stars do you give your work?

Notes:_____

Reading Time!

Choose a few books from your stack to focus on today. Write down or draw anything that inspires you.

Screen Time

Watch a cooking show, high-quality film, video, documentary, or baking tutorial.

Title_____

Screen Time_____

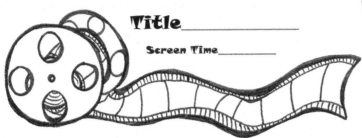

Notes

Take notes on what you are learning.

_____
_____
_____
_____
_____
_____
_____

Rating:

Worst

Bad

Awful

Ok

Nice

Great

Best

Math Practice

Use this page for math practice, graphic design, and creative measurements. If you have a book on mathematics use this page for notes.

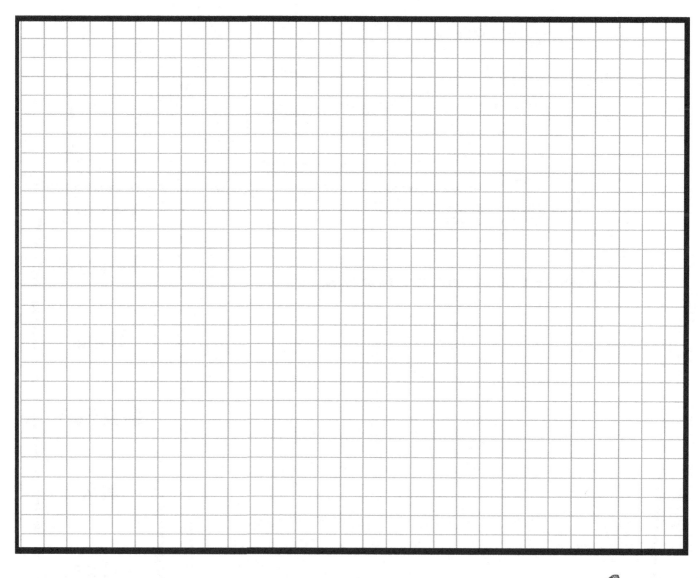

Notes:_____

_____

_____

_____

_____

_____

_____

_____

Baking Dreams

Design something beautiful you want to bake!

Look at photos in your cookbooks or online for ideas.

Notes:_____

_____

_____

_____

_____

_____

SINCE 1991

BAKERY
• PREMIUM GOODS •

Fluffy Blueberry Muffins

Ingredients

- 2 cups all-purpose flour
- 2 tsp baking powder
- 3/4 tsp salt
- 1/2 cup unsalted-butter melted
- 1 cup granulated sugar
- 2 eggs
- 2 tsp vanilla extract
- 1/2 cup milk
- 2 cups blueberries

Instructions

Preheat oven to 350°F.
Line a muffin tin with paper liners.
Cooking spray the liners along with the pan with spray.
In a medium bowl, mix together the flour, baking powder, and salt. whisk to blend.
With an electric mixer, beat the butter, vanilla, milk, and granulated sugar for around two minutes until becomes light and creamy.
Add eggs one at a time, beating well after each addition and then scraping down the sides of the bowl.
(The batter may seem somewhat grainy – that is fine).
The batter will thicken.
Add the blueberries and fold gently with a spatula until evenly dispersed. Scoop 1/3 cups into the muffin trays and bake for 15-20 minutes. Serve warm and Enjoy!

Baking Time!

Notes: _____

_____

_____

_____

_____

_____

Plans & Priorities

Date:_____

To-do List:
_____
_____
_____
_____
_____

A Quote:
_____
_____
_____
_____
_____

Shopping List:
_____
_____
_____
_____
_____

My Plans:
_____
_____
_____
_____
_____

I am Thankful for:
_____
_____
_____
_____

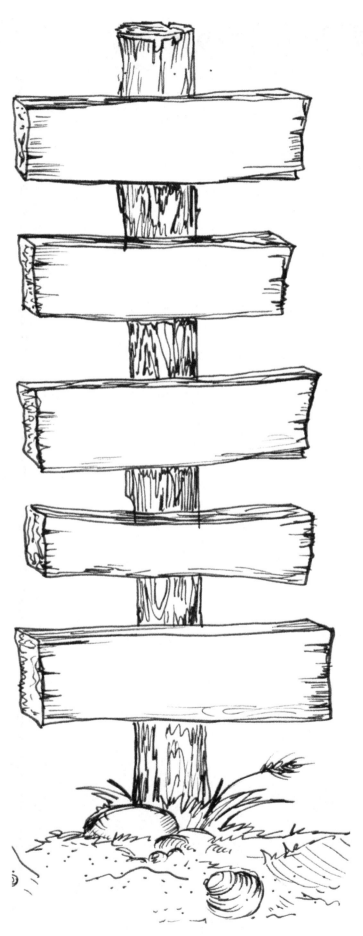

DESIGN SIGNS FOR YOUR BAKERY

Baking Challenge

Bake cinnamon rolls, top the hot rolls with vanilla ice cream
and then watch a Disney movie with your family.

Draw what you've made!

How many stars do you give your work?

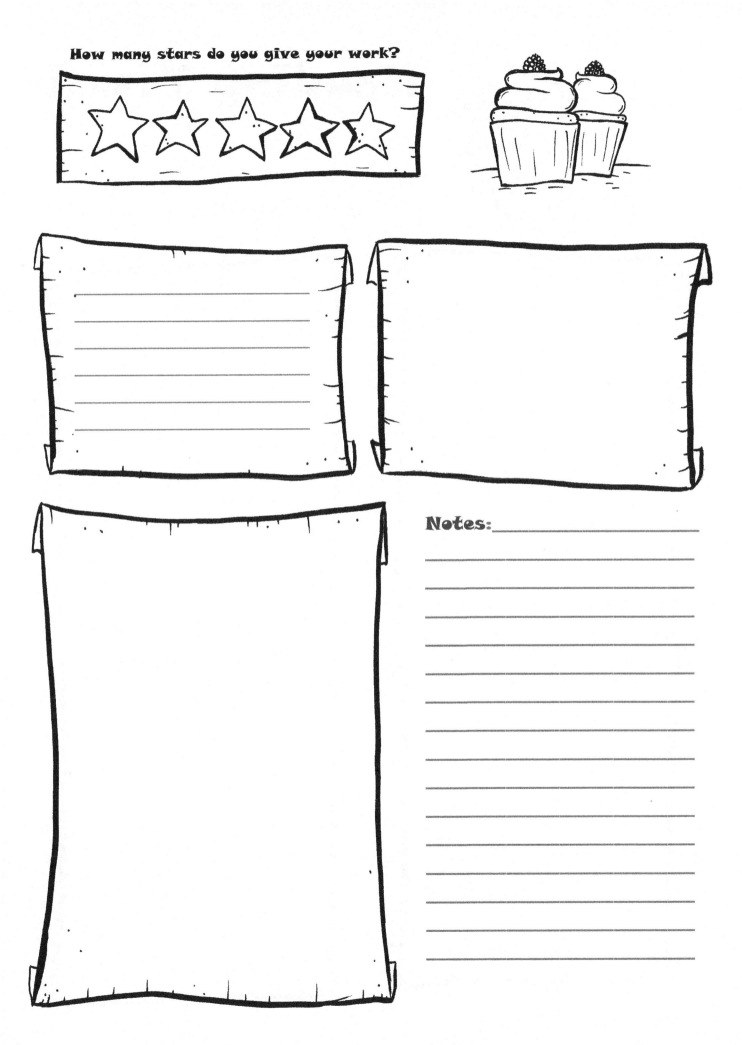

Notes: _____
_____
_____
_____
_____
_____
_____
_____
_____
_____
_____
_____
_____
_____
_____

Reading Time!

Choose a few books from your stack
to focus on today. Write down or draw
anything that inspires you.

Screen Time

Watch a cooking show, high-quality film, video, documentary, or baking tutorial.

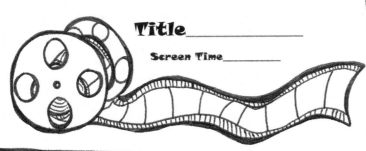

Title_____

Screen Time_____

Notes

Take notes on what you are learning.

_____

_____

_____

_____

_____

_____

_____

Rating:

Worst

Bad

Awful

Ok

Nice

Great

Best

Math Practice

Use this page for math practice, graphic design, and creative measurements. If you have a book on mathematics use this page for notes.

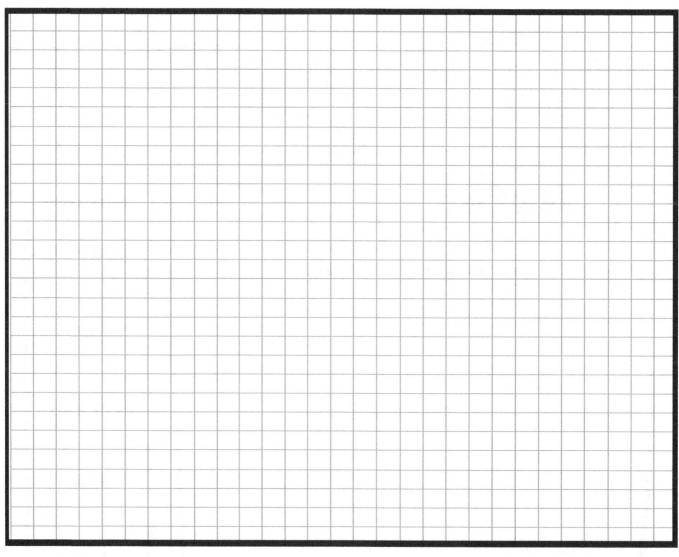

Notes:_____

_____

_____

_____

_____

_____

_____

_____

_____

Baking Dreams

Design something beautiful you want to bake!

Look at photos in your cookbooks or online for ideas.

Notes:_____

_____

_____

_____

_____

_____

SINCE 1991

BAKERY

• PREMIUM GOODS •

Best Banana Bread

Ingredients

1 1/2 cups banana mashed

2 cup all-purpose flour

3/4 cup brown sugar

2 eggs large

1/2 cup butter

1 tbsp milk

1 tsp baking soda

1/4 tsp salt

1 1/2 tsp vanilla

1 tsp ground cinnamon

Optional: 3/4 cup chopped pecans

Instructions

Preheat oven to 350°F. Butter a 9 x 5 loaf pan.
Put the flour, baking soda, cinnamon, and salt in a bowl and mix together.
Separately, mix the butter and the sugar until creamy.
Then add the eggs one at a time and mix.
Now add the milk, vanilla extract, and mashed bananas and mix.
Put this mixture into the flour mixture and blend. Pour batter into prepared loaf pan and bake for 60-70 minutes.
Let it cool for 10 minutes in the pan.

How many stars do you give this recipe?

Baking Time!

Notes: _____
_____
_____
_____
_____
_____

**Draw a picture of
your baking creation!**

Plans & Priorities

Date:_____

To-do List:
_____
_____
_____
_____

A Quote:
_____
_____
_____
_____

Shopping List:
_____
_____
_____
_____

My Plans:
_____
_____
_____
_____

I am Thankful for:

_____
_____
_____
_____

Relax & Be Creative

Baking Challenge

Bake a buttery cobbler. Blueberry, Apple, peach, blackberry or raspberry? You choose.

Draw what you've made!

How many stars do you give your work?

Notes:_____

Reading Time!

Choose a few books from your stack to focus on today. Write down or draw anything that inspires you.

Screen Time

Watch a cooking show, high-quality film, video, documentary, or baking tutorial.

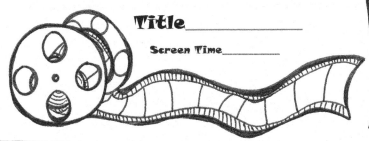

Title_____

Screen Time_____

Notes

Take notes on what you are learning.

_____

_____

_____

_____

_____

_____

_____

Rating:

Worst

Bad

Awful

Ok

Nice

Great

Best

Math Practice

Use this page for math practice, graphic design,
and creative measurements. If you have a book on
mathematics use this page for notes.

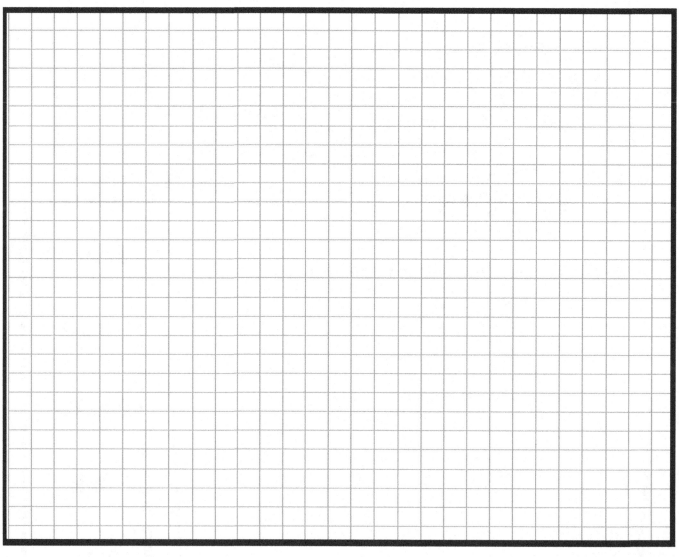

Notes:_____

_____

_____

_____

_____

_____

_____

Baking Dreams

Design something beautiful you want to bake!

Look at photos in your cookbooks or online for ideas.

Notes:_____

_____

_____

_____

_____

_____

SINCE 1991

BAKERY
• PREMIUM GOODS •

Mo-Mo's Oreo Cheesecake

Ingredients

- 24 Oreos
- 4 tbsp butter, melted
- 16 ounces cream cheese
- 1 cup powdered sugar
- 1 1/2 tsp vanilla extract
- 2 cups heavy cream, cold
- 16 Oreos, chopped

Instructions

To make the crust:
Insert the Oreos into a food processor and process until you have fine crumbs.

Scoop the crumbs into the butter and a bowl and blend until are of those crumbs are moistened.

Line the base of a 9-inch pan with parchment paper, scoop the mixture into the pan, and firmly press it into a single layer. Transfer the crust to the refrigerator to cool while you make the filling.
Utilizing a stand mixer fitted with the whisk attachment or a big mixing bowl with a handheld mixer, beat the cream cheese until smooth. Add the sugar and vanilla extract and blend until well mixed. Start on low then increase the rate to medium-high until stiff peaks and the mix thickens.

Add the cream and fold it in until blended or blend it . Fold in the cream then the chopped Oreos.

How many stars do you give this recipe?

Baking Time!

Notes:_____

_____

_____

_____

_____

_____

Draw a picture of
your baking creation!

Plans & Priorities

Date:_____

To-do List:

_____
_____
_____
_____

A Quote:

_____
_____
_____
_____
_____

Shopping List:

_____
_____
_____
_____

My Plans:

_____
_____
_____
_____

I am Thankful for:

_____
_____
_____
_____

DESIGN MENUS FOR YOUR BAKERY

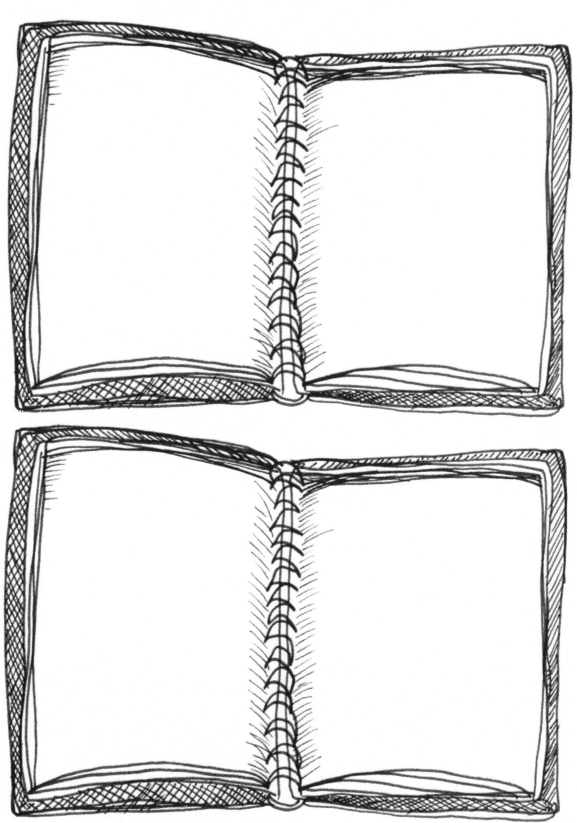

Baking Challenge

Bake something for your neighbors:

Draw what you've made!

How many stars do you give your work?

Notes:_____

Reading Time!

Choose a few books from your stack to focus on today. Write down or draw anything that inspires you.

Screen Time

Watch a cooking show, high-quality film, video, documentary, or baking tutorial.

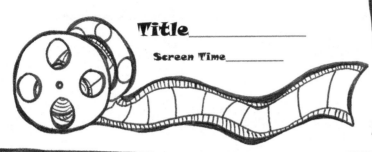

Title_____

Screen Time_____

Notes

Take notes on what you are learning.

_____
_____
_____
_____
_____
_____
_____

Rating:

Worst

Bad

Awful

Ok

Nice

Great

Best

Math Practice

Use this page for math practice, graphic design, and creative measurements. If you have a book on mathematics use this page for notes.

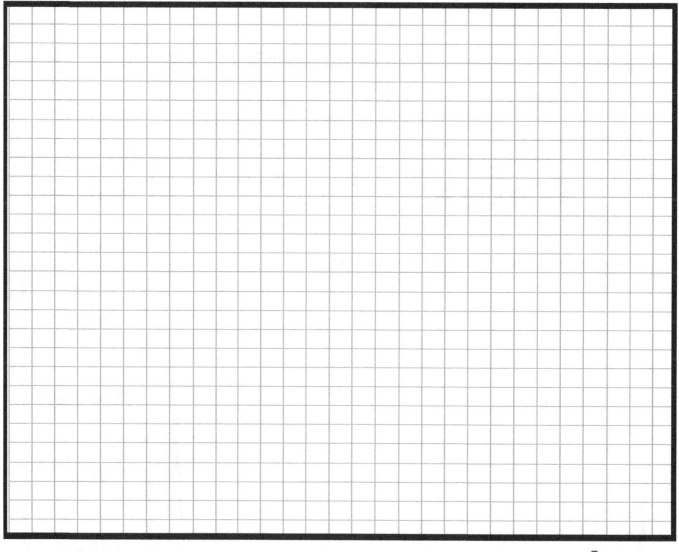

Notes:_____

_____

_____

_____

_____

_____

_____

_____

Baking Dreams

Design something beautiful you want to bake!

Look at photos in your cookbooks or online for ideas.

Notes:_____

_____

_____

_____

_____

_____

SINCE 1991

BAKERY

• PREMIUM GOODS •

Buttery Drop Biscuits

Ingredients

2 cups all purpose flour

1 tbsp baking powder

1 tsp sugar

1/2 tsp salt

1/2 tsp garlic powder

1/2 tsp paprika (optional)

1 stick butter, melted

3/4 cup milk

Instructions

Preheat oven to 425°F.

Prepare a large baking sheet with non-stick cooking spray or parchment paper and set aside.

In a large bowl, whisk together the flour, baking powder, sugar, salt, paprika, and garlic powder.

Stir the butter and milk into the flour mixture just until moistened.

Drop the batter by heaping tablespoons onto prepared baking sheet.

Bake for 9-11 minutes until golden.

Slather with butter, eat and enjoy!

How many stars do you give this recipe?

Baking Time!

Notes:_____

_____

_____

_____

_____

_____

**Draw a picture of
your baking creation!**

Plans & Priorities

Date:_____

To-do List:
_____
_____
_____
_____

A Quote:
_____
_____
_____
_____

Shopping List:
_____
_____
_____
_____

My Plans:
_____
_____
_____

I am Thankful for:

_____
_____
_____
_____

Baking Challenge

Make layered cookie mousse parfaits. Go to the store and pick out a few different cookie packages: Oreos, mini chocolate chips or Nutter Butters. Also get pudding and whipped cream. Go home and find a few little cups. Be creative, the rest is up to you!

Draw what you've made!

How many stars do you give your work?

Notes:_____

Reading Time!

Choose a few books from your stack to focus on today. Write down or draw anything that inspires you.

Screen Time

Watch a cooking show, high-quality film,
video, documentary, or baking tutorial.

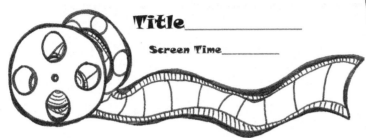

Title_____

Screen Time_____

Notes

Take notes on what you are learning.

_____
_____
_____
_____
_____
_____
_____

Rating:

Worst

Bad

Awful

Ok

Nice

Great

Best

Math Practice

Use this page for math practice, graphic design, and creative measurements. If you have a book on mathematics use this page for notes.

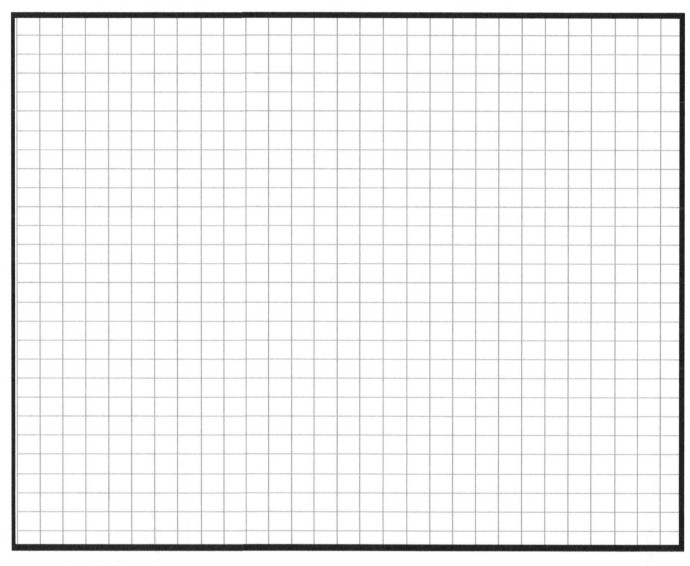

Notes:_____

_____

_____

_____

_____

_____

_____

Baking Dreams

Design something beautiful you want to bake!

Look at photos in your cookbooks or online for ideas.

Notes:_____

_____

_____

_____

_____

_____

_____

SINCE 1991

BAKERY

• PREMIUM GOODS •

The Chewiest Sugar Cookies

Ingredients

- 1 cup butter, softened

- 1 cup granulated sugar

- 1 egg

- 2 tsp vanilla

- 1/2 tsp almond extract (optional, but it adds an extra flavor)

- 2 1/2 cups all purpose flour

- 1/2 tsp baking soda

- 1/2 tsp baking powder

- 1/4 tsp salt

- **Topping**
- 1/4 cup granulated sugar, for dipping

Instructions

Preheat oven to 350°F.

Line a baking sheet with parchment paper or coat with baking spray.

In a large bowl, cream butter and sugar together until light and fluffy, about 1 minute. Add in the egg, vanilla extract, and almond extract. Beat until combined.

Add in flour, baking soda, baking powder, and salt. Mix until just combined, making sure to scrape down the sides of the bowl every now and again.

Roll dough into 1" balls and roll in sugar.

Place on baking sheet, about 2" apart.

Bake for 10-11 minutes or until cookies have set.

Allow to cool. Enjoy with friends or family!

How many stars do you give this recipe?

Baking Time!

Notes: _____

_____

_____

_____

_____

_____

Draw a picture of your baking creation!

Plans & Priorities

Date:_____

To-do List:
_____
_____
_____
_____

A Quote:
_____
_____
_____
_____

Shopping List:
_____
_____
_____
_____

My Plans:
_____
_____
_____
_____

I am Thankful for:
_____
_____
_____
_____

DESIGN BAKERY LOGOS
FOR YOUR T-SHIRTS

Baking Challenge

Research and make edible cookie dough..
(Of course, all our parents grew up
eating cookie dough with the raw egg, right?)

Draw what you've made!

How many stars do you give your work?

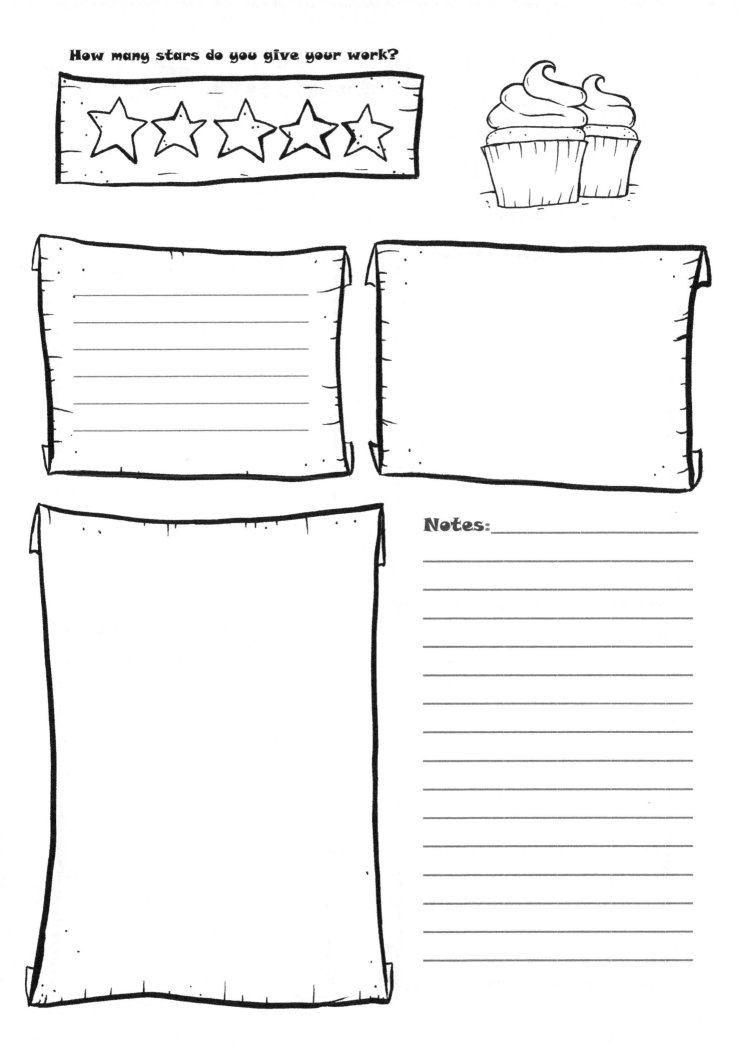

Notes:_____

Reading Time!

Choose a few books from your stack to focus on today. Write down or draw anything that inspires you.

Screen Time

Watch a cooking show, high-quality film, video, documentary, or baking tutorial.

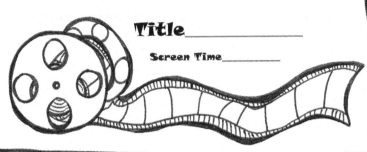

Title_____

Screen Time_____

Notes

Take notes on what you are learning.

_____

_____

_____

_____

_____

_____

_____

Rating:

Worst

Bad

Awful

Ok

Nice

Great

Best

Math Practice

Use this page for math practice, graphic design, and creative measurements. If you have a book on mathematics use this page for notes.

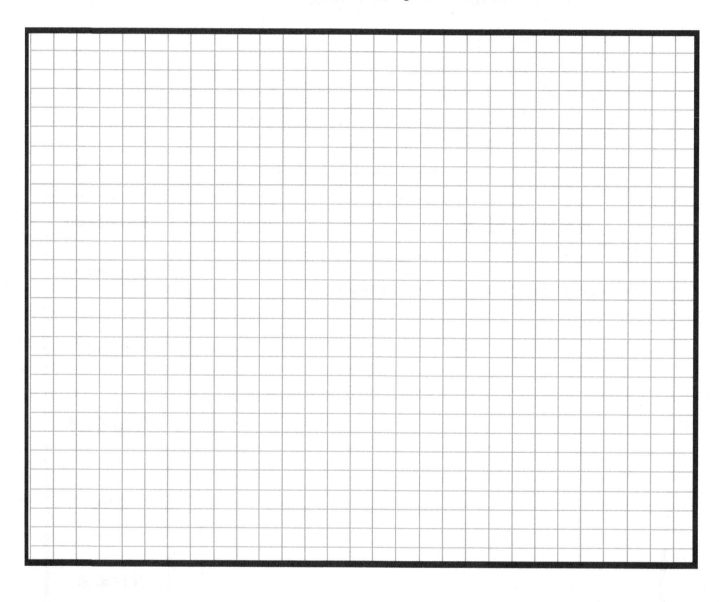

Notes:_____

_____

_____

_____

_____

_____

_____

_____

Baking Dreams

Design something beautiful you want to bake!

Look at photos in your cookbooks or online for ideas.

Notes:_____

_____

_____

_____

_____

_____

SINCE   1991

BAKERY

• PREMIUM GOODS •

Papa's Peanut Butter Cookies

Ingredients

- 1 cup creamy peanut butter

- 1/2 cup butter, softened

- 1/2 cup white sugar

- 1/2 cup brown sugar

- 1 egg

- 1 tbsp vanilla extract

- 1 1/2 cups flour

- 1 tsp baking soda

- 1/4 tsp salt

Instructions

Preheat the oven to 350°F.
Line 2 baking pans with parchment paper, if desired.
In a large mixing bowl, cream together the peanut butter, butter,
sugar, and brown sugar.
Beat together until smooth & creamy (best if using a stand mixer or hand mixer.)
Add the egg and vanilla extract and continue to mix until well combined.
In a small mixing bowl, whisk together the flour, baking soda, and salt. Stir the
flour mixture into the butter and sugar mixture and mix until well combined.
Use a cookie dough scooper or spoon the dough into 1-inch balls.
Roll them in white granulated sugar if you desire and place on to baking sheets.
Using a fork, press down on each ball of dough to flatten,
creating a criss-cross pattern.
Bake for 8-9 minutes. Do not over bake. Let cool on the baking sheet for a few
minutes and then transfer to a wire rack.
These keep well for a couple of days in an airtight container.

How many stars do you give this recipe?

Baking Time!

Notes:_____

_____

_____

_____

_____

_____

**Draw a picture of
your baking creation!**

Fun-Schooling With Thinking Tree Books

Copyright Information:

Contact Us:

The Thinking Tree, LLC
+1 (USA)   317.622.8852

info@funschooling.com

FunSchooling.com

Made in the USA
Monee, IL
14 August 2021